COMMON BRITISH
GRASSES AND LEGUMES

COMMON BRITISH
GRASSES AND LEGUMES

BY

J. O. THOMAS, M.Sc., N.D.A., N.D.D.
(Principal, Lackham School of Agriculture, Wilts.)

AND

L. J. DAVIES

WITH 50 ILLUSTRATIONS

1724

LONGMANS

LONGMANS, GREEN AND CO LTD
48 Grosvenor Street, London W.1
*Associated companies, branches and representatives
throughout the world*

Printed in Great Britain by
Lowe and Brydone (Printers) Limited, London N.W.10

PREFACE

This book contains a general description of the common grasses and legumes with which the British farmer is concerned. It is intended as a guide to the identification of the various species in the field, and has been written to meet the needs of agricultural colleges, farm institutes, young farmers' classes and schools.

The authors are indebted to Professor R. A. Roberts, Mr G. W. Olive, C.B.E., M.A. and to various members of the Welsh Plant Breeding Station for taking a practical interest in the preparation of the book; to the late Professor S. P. Mercer for supplying the keys to the vegetative organs of both grasses and legumes; and to Mr H. J. Goddard (Dunns Farm Seeds, Ltd.), Mr Frank Hughes and the late Mr T. A. Dymes for supplying material.

They are also indebted to Mr T. H. Davies, B.Sc. for improvements in the second edition and to Mr B. W. H. Coulson, M.A. for valuable assistance with the proofs.

Helpful suggestions for improvements in the fourth edition have been received from Mr J. S. Hall, B.Sc., Professor Ian Moore, C.B.E., Ph.D., Mr S. J. Willis, B.Sc. and Mr P. Lyth, B.Sc., The authors are also grateful to Mr A. Voysey, M.B.E. B.Sc. for valuable assistance with the proofs in the fourth edition.

J. O. T.
L. J. D.

CONTENTS

CHAPTER 1

THE MORPHOLOGY OF SOME COMMON BRITISH GRASSES

(For the meaning of unfamiliar technical terms, the reader is advised to refer to the Glossary on page 115.)

THE morphological features of the grasses may be studied under two headings: (*a*) the floral organs, and (*b*) the vegetative organs.

The Floral Organs.

The flowers of grasses, although not conspicuous, possess all those parts which are essential for the production of seed. They are usually grouped together to form numerous spikelets, which are arranged in a racemose order, on a main stem or culm to form the inflorescence (Fig. 1 A).

The Inflorescence.—The form of the inflorescence varies greatly in different species, and is determined by the way in which the spikelets are attached to the main axis. In some species the spikelets are borne directly upon the main stem, forming an inflorescence termed a spike (Fig. 1 A), whereas in others they are borne on short simple branches to form a raceme or spike-like panicle (Fig. 6 A). In many cases the spikelets are supported on secondary, tertiary and further divided branches to form a panicle (Fig. 5 A) that is close, spreading or drooping, according to the relative lengths of its branches.

The Spikelet.—A spikelet normally consists of an axis, at the base of which are borne a pair of opposite bracts, commonly called the outer and inner empty glumes. These glumes, although usually two in number, may vary from one in Italian Rye-grass (Fig. 1 B) to four in Sweet Vernal (Fig. 8).

Immediately above the empty glumes, and arranged in a similar manner, are two further bracts, termed the outer and inner pales*, and in between which lies the actual flower (Fig. 1 C). The pales often differ from the empty glumes in possessing bristle-like structures called awns (Fig. 1 E). These may be terminal, dorsal or basal, according to whether they arise from the tip, middle or base of the pale.

*Also called the lemma and the palea respectively; though in this book the original names are retained.

1

The number of flowers in each spikelet varies from one to several in different species, e.g. Timothy and Tall Oat Grass always possess one and two flowers respectively, while in Italian Rye-grass there may be several flowers per spikelet (Fig. 1 c).

The Flower.—A typical flower (Fig. 1 D), which is protected on each side by the outer and inner pales, is composed of three hypogynous stamens (except in Sweet Vernal which possesses two) and one carpel. At the base of the ovary are two small scale-like structures termed lodicules, which may be clearly seen during the time of fertilisation. The filaments of the stamens are long and slender, and are attached to long anthers. The carpel consists of a small ovoid ovary, which frequently bears a pair of divergent feathery stigmas at its apex.

Grasses are wind-pollinated and cross-fertilised, though self-fertilisation often occurs. At the time of flowering the lodicules swell and spread apart the pales, thus exposing the feathery stigmas. About the same time the filaments of the stamens grow rapidly, and push out the anthers. The anthers then burst, and the pollen grains are distributed by the wind and caught by the feathery stigmas of other grasses to pollinate only those of the same species. In a short time afterwards the pales close up on the fertilised ovary, which then develops into a fruit. In some cases, such as Wheat, the flowers are cleistogamous, and fertilisation is often accomplished before the opening of the pales.

The Fruit or Commercial Seed.—During its formation the seed-coat fuses with the ovary wall to form a one-seeded fruit (commonly called a seed), termed a " caryopsis "; a typical example of this is seen in the wheat grain (Fig. 2 A). In the majority of species of grasses, however, the pales so closely invest the caryopsis that they become almost fused to the ovary wall (Fig. 1 E). In a few other cases the caryopsis, although enveloped by the pales, is not fused and easily separated, e.g. Timothy Grass (Fig. 26 c).

When ripe the rachis of the spikelet in grasses usually breaks off at a point near the base of the fruit. In those cases where

FIG. I.—A. Inflorescence of Italian Rye-grass. B. Spikelet. C. Diagram of flowers on spikelet. D. Individual flower. E. Fruit or commercial seed.
1. Rachis; 2. outer glume; 3. awn; 4. outer pale; 5. inner pale; 6. rachilla; 7. ovary; 8. stigmas; 9. filament; 10. anthers; 11. lodicules.

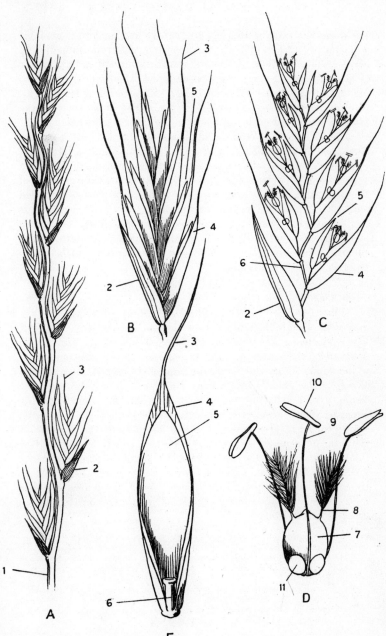

the pales are present there is frequently attached to each fruit a portion of the rachis which supported the fruit immediately above. This little stalk-like structure is termed a " rachilla " (Fig. 1 E), and is often a useful diagnostic feature on the commercial seed. In a few instances, e.g. Yorkshire Fog (Fig. 21 B), the commercial seed consists of the entire spikelet with the glumes, pales and grains of one or more flowers attached.

The True Seed.—When a longitudinal section is cut the true seed may be examined (Fig. 2 A). This consists of a large proportion of starchy endosperm with a small embryo enclosed within a seed-coat or testa. The embryo is situated near the base of the seed, and is separated from the endosperm by a thin-walled shield-like structure, called the scutellum or cotyledon. It is composed of a short primary shoot (the plumule), a primary root (the radicle), and two pairs of secondary rootlets. Both plumule and radicle are enclosed within a sheath, which is continuous with the scutellum.

Germination.

When provided with an adequate supply of water and air, and with a suitable temperature the seeds begin to germinate. The endosperm is converted into simple sugars by an enzyme secreted by the scutellum, and transferred to the growing points of the young embryo. The young temporary rootlets then emerge through the sheath (*coleorhiza*) and assist in establishing the young seedling in the soil (Fig. 2 B). At the same time the plumule sheath (*coleoptile*) appears above the soil as a delicate, white tube-like structure. After a short time the temporary rootlets are replaced by permanent ones, which arise from the lowermost node of the stem, and the plumule pushes its first green leaf (Fig. 2 C, D, E) through a slit at the apex of the coleoptile. By this time practically the whole of the endosperm has been utilised by the embryo, and the plant is about to lead an independent existence.

FIG. 2.—A. Longitudinal section through caryopsis of Wheat. B. First stage in germination of Wheat. C. Second stage in germination of Wheat. D. Second stage in germination of Barley. E. Second stage in germination of Perennial Rye.grass. F. Third stage in germination of Wheat.
1. Ovary wall; 2. seed-coat; 3. scutellum; 4. endosperm; 5. plumule; 6. radicle; 7. secondary rootlets; 8. coleorhiza; 9. coleoptile; 10. permanent rootlets; 11. first green leaf; 12. first internode; 13. tillers; 14. leaf sheath; 15. leaf blade.

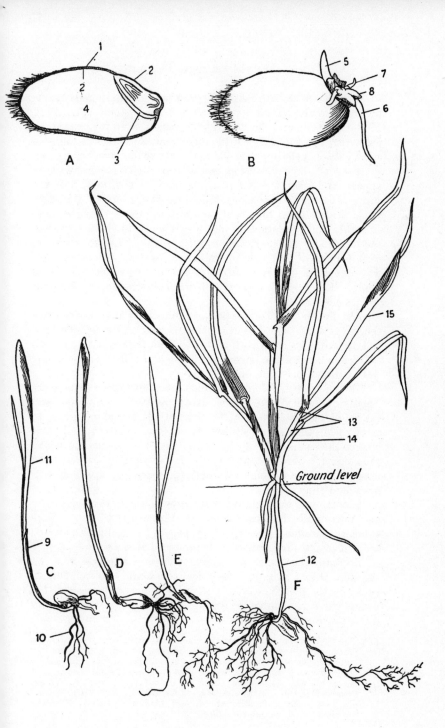

A

B

C   D   E   F

Ground level

1
2
2
4
3

5
7
8
6

11
9
10

15

13
14

12

In fruits, such as wheat and rye, where the pales are absent, the roots and plumule emerge at the same point (Fig. 2 B). In Barley, Oats and the majority of grasses, however, where the pales remain attached, the plumule grows up beneath the pale and emerges at the opposite end to the young rootlets (Fig. 2 D, E). A second stage of development is seen when more green leaves appear, and when the terminal bud finds its own level near the surface of the soil by an elongation of the first internode (Fig. 2 F). If the seed is sown too deeply the first internode elongates considerably and appears as a long wiry stem. In shallow sowing, the internodes are short and scarcely visible. Lateral buds are next formed in the axils of the leaves, which later break their way out from the enclosing leaf sheath to produce shoots or tillers. The tillering capacity of grasses varies in the different species and strains.

The Young Shoot.—This consists of a short stem upon which the young leaves are crowded and protected on the outside by a leaf sheath. Its shape, which varies from flattened to cylindrical, depends upon the degree of folding and rolling of the young leaf blades (Fig. 3 A, B, C).

The older stems of grasses which later bear inflorescences are usually cylindrical and hollow, except at the nodes which form the point of attachment of the leaves. If the stems grow up erect within their sheaths (intravaginal branching) a tufted habit of growth results (Fig. 8 D). If, on the other hand, the young shoots pierce through the sheaths in which they are enclosed (extravaginal branching) a straggly or spreading appearance is presented (Fig. 4 D).

In some species, stems other than the flowering ones may grow out horizontally to form stolons or rhizomes (Fig. 7 D). Such stoloniferous plants are able to propagate themselves rapidly on account of the adventitious roots produced at the nodes.

Leaves.—The leaves are arranged in two alternate rows on the stem (Fig. 3 D, E, F). Each leaf consists of two well-defined parts, (a) the sheath or lower portion attached to the stem at the nodes and surrounding the young leaves, and (b) the blade or upper portion which is free.

FIG. 3.—A. Section through young shoot of Italian Rye-grass showing rolled leaves and split sheath. B. Section through young shoot of Crested Dogstail showing folded leaves and split sheath. C. Section through young shoot of Cocksfoot showing shoot of folded leaves and entire sheath. D. Young shoot of Italian Rye-grass. E. Young Crested Dogstail. F. Young shoot of Cocksfoot.
1. Split leaf sheath ; 2. auricles ; 3. leaf blade ; 4. ligule ; 5. entire leaf sheath : 6. vascular bundles.

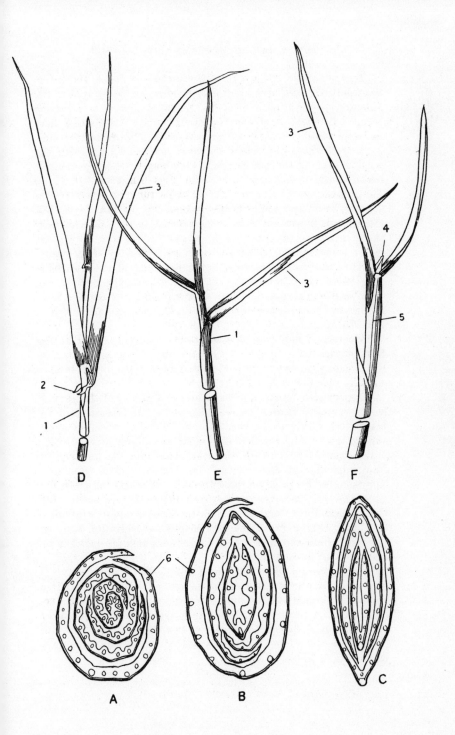

Leaf Sheath.—This is a tubular structure enclosing the lowermost portion of the stem, and may be either entire or split in the different species (Fig. 3 D, E, F). In many grasses a colouring pigment develops on the basal portion of the sheath, which may be either present over the entire surface or confined to the veins.

Leaf Blades.—The blades or laminæ are continuous with the upper portion of the leaf sheath. They may be either expanded, folded, rolled or solid and bristle-like (Figs. 6 E, 20 E, 7 E, 17 E). The presence or absence of ribs or veins running parallel from apex to base can usually be determined by the naked eye, but these are best studied from microscopical sections of the blade (Fig. 4 G).

In some species the veins are surrounded by thick-walled cells to form prominent ridges on the surface of the leaf blade (Fig. 16 G). In others, these ridges are small and inconspicuous (Fig. 15 G). There is, however, in the majority of cases a midrib on the under surface of the blade, when it is said to be keeled (Fig. 15 G).

A series of modified cells are always present, either at the base of each rib or flanking the mid-rib. These are known as motor cells, and can often be detected as transparent white lines when the blade is held up to the light (19 E).

The breadth, length and the degree of tapering of the apex of leaves vary in different grasses. The colour and hairiness of the blade often vary with age and habitat. In many cases the upper surface is dull, and the underside distinctly glossy and smooth.

Auricles.—The base of the leaf blade may be modified to form ledge-like processes on each side termed auricles (Fig. 3 D). They may be long and clasping the stem, or small and lobed.

Ligule.—At the junction between the leaf blade and sheath there is usually a small erect semi-transparent outgrowth called the ligule (Fig. 3 F). It may be long, short, serrated, blunt or pointed. Both the auricle and ligule characters are peculiar to, and constant in each species.

Root System.—When the young grass plant begins to unfold its leaves the primary rootlets of the embryo disappear, and are succeeded by adventitious roots which grow out from the lowermost nodes of the stem. These are usually numerous and very much branched, forming a dense tuft near the surface of the soil (Fig. 5 D). The length, fineness and colour of the roots vary slightly in different grasses.

CHAPTER 2

CHARACTERS THAT INFLUENCE THE ECONOMIC VALUE OF GRASSES

GRASSES are generally classified as useful or useless by the farmer according to their particular value. Although there are over one hundred different types of British grasses, only about twenty are of any real agricultural value.

In general, the value of a species or variety will depend upon the following characteristics : (a) Productivity or yield, (b) Persistency, (c) Chemical composition, (d) Palatability, and (e) Winter greenness.

Productivity.

The weight of produce obtained from any one species or variety will largely depend upon the length of the growing period and its tillering capacity. Perennial Rye-grass is said to be highly productive because it tillers freely and grows from early spring until late autumn, whereas Tall Oat Grass, on the other hand, grows for a short period only and yields comparatively little bulk. Productivity is also influenced by the intensity of recovery after grazing or cutting, since these factors are more favourable to the growth of young tillers in some species than in others.

Persistency.

Grasses, such as Perennial Rye-grass, Cocksfoot, Meadow Fescue and Timothy, live for a considerable number of years in a suitable environment, whereas Italian Rye-grass and Short-rotation Rye-grass usually disappear after one or two seasons, irrespective of the surroundings. This indicates that before sowing seed mixtures for either temporary or permanent pastures, a study of the persistency of each species or variety is of the utmost importance.

Chemical Composition and Leafiness.

The value of a grass depends to a great extent upon the amount of proteins, minerals, fats and carbohydrates present. Recent research has proved that the leaves possess a higher percentage of proteins and minerals than the stems, and that a species or variety with a high proportion of young leaves is extremely valuable from a feeding point of view. The majority of grasses become stemmy with age, but some types produce numerous stems early in life, which renders them valueless to the farmer.

Palatability.

Although a species or variety may be highly productive and persistent, with a satisfactory chemical composition, it may on account of its harsh or hairy leaves be unpalatable, and left unconsumed by stock, especially when in an advanced stage. Yorkshire Fog is an example of such a plant that would otherwise be a valuable component of seed mixtures.

Winter Greenness.

The value of a species will also largely depend upon its capacity to remain green during the winter months. Unfortunately most of the British grasses remain dormant, and leaf production is at a minimum during this period. Recent research has, however, indicated that young leys composed of indigenous varieties remain greener and are far more productive in winter than most old permanent pastures. Certain varieties of Tall Fescue and Red Fescue have already been bred to yield a fair amount of leaf during February and March, and further work is in progress to produce winter green strains of different species to suit a wide range of conditions. Some permanent pastures with a high proportion of indigenous Perennial Rye-grass and Crested Dogstail remain surprisingly green throughout the winter.

Plant Improvement.

Within a single species there are varieties that differ from one another in many ways. Thus, Perennial Rye-grass appears in some districts to be tufted, stemmy and short-lived, while elsewhere a more leafy and persistent type exists. These and many other differences in character were first used by Sir George Stapledon at the Welsh Plant Breeding Station to breed types or varieties of single species to suit different environments and circumstances. These are the famous "S" varieties.

He soon discovered that the wild, indigenous, British species were superior in many ways to the imported, commercial ones from abroad; with the result that plant breeders in this and other countries have evolved, by selection and hybridisation, numerous varieties of many grasses, as well as varieties of Red and White Clovers and Lucerne, amongst which can be found one to suit any environment or system of management.

In order to achieve this, plant breeders have taken into account many characteristics of the grass plant: productivity, persistency, palatability, digestibility, leafiness, growth in spring and autumn, winter hardiness, speed of germination and establishment, compatability with other varieties and species, aggressiveness, resistance to drought and disease, etc.

Most of these new varieties can, broadly speaking, be grouped according to their time of flowering as Early, Mid-season and Late. This is useful, as there seems to be some correlation of time of flowering with maximum growth; the late-flowering varieties being more leafy (and therefore less stemmy) and more prostrate than the early-flowering ones, and better suited to long leys.

In addition to many pedigree "S" varieties bred at Aberystwyth, some useful grasses have come from New Zealand, the Netherlands, Belgium, Norway and Sweden. However, it is beyond the scope of this book to deal with the qualities of all the varieties of all the species evolved by plant breeding stations throughout the world, and whose seed is now appearing on the British market. So the farmer can now make up a seeds mixture that will suit his environment, lengthen the growing season, and fulfil his purpose, whether that be to graze stock or to make hay, silage or dried grass.

Thus, for example, he would choose a variety of Tall Fescue for very early spring grazing; varieties of Italian Rye-grass and Short-rotation Rye-grasses for slightly later grazing; varieties of Timothy, Meadow Fescue and Red Clover for summer growth; and possibly varieties of Cocksfoot and Perennial Rye-grass for the autumn. For silage, varieties of White Clover and Lucerne would be suitable, and to give foggage up to Christmas some varieties of Cocksfoot might be included.

These varieties, bred at Aberystwyth, are often referred to, in speech and writing, by their numbers alone. They are tabulated on page 117.

2

Chapter 3

KEY TO THE VEGETATIVE CHARACTERS OF SOME COMMON GRASSES

I. *Leaf needle-like* and not easily flattened out.

(Leaves of several grasses may assume needle-like form, but are easily unfolded or unrolled.)

A. Leaf distinctly folded (V section).

    (*a*) Ligule very short ; leaf delicate
                            Festuca ovina and F. duriuscula.

    (*b*) Ligule very small ; leaves sometimes hairy ; inclined to creep   .   .   .   .   .   . *Festuca rubra.*

    (*c*) Ligule prominent ; leaf hard, glaucous, upright ; roots wiry   .   .   .   .   .   . *Nardus stricta.*

B. Leaf practically solid, delicate (wheat grain section) ; roots red   .   .   .   .   . *Deschampsia flexuosa.*

II. *Leaf flat*, or if needle-like easily flattened out.

A. Leaf folded in bud ; shoot more or less flat.

    (*a*) Small claws at base of leaf ; basal sheaths smooth, shining pink ; ligule very short ; blade markedly ribbed above
                            Lolium perenne.
    (Occasional plants have some tillers folded and some rolled.)

    (*b*) No claws at base of leaf.

      1. Aquatic grass with large leaves.

        (i) Sheath keeled ; blade yellowish-green, with yellow triangles at base ; prominently ribbed
                            Glyceria fluitans.

        (ii) Sheath not keeled ; blade not prominently ribbed ; plant reedy   .   .   . *Glyceria maxima.*

      2. Plants not aquatic.

        (i) Leaf smooth, ribless, with two whitish median lines ; hooded tip.

(1) Leaf stiff, glaucous ; ligule very short (mountain limestone hills—in north and west) *Sesleria caerulea.*

(2) Leaf not stiff, not glaucous.

    (a) Stem flattened ; ligule long ; blade shining below ; apex pointed ; plant usually tufted ; minute asperities on leaf sheath . *Poa trivialis.*

    (b) Stem rough ; ligule long ; blade dull underneath, often wrinkled transversely ; plant tufted (in flower all the year round) . . *Poa annua.*

    (c) Ligule short ; apex of blade blunt ; plant markedly stoloniferous ; no asperities on sheath *Poa pratensis.*

(Intermediate forms between *P. pratensis* and *P. trivialis* are common.)

    (ii) Leaf without median white lines.

(1) Sheath or blade or both hairy.

    (a) Ligule long, membraneous ; sheath hirsute (hedge banks) . . . . . *Avena pubescens.*

    (b) Ligule a tuft of hairs ; long soft hairs sparsely scattered along edge and underside of leaf (poor and dry pastures) . . *Sieglingia decumbens.*

(2) Sheath and blade smooth.

    (a) Seaside grass. Leaves hard, usually rolled up ; ligule long, bifid ; markedly stoloniferous *Ammophila arenaria.*

    (b) Stem very flat and sharp edged ; ligule long, plant tufted . . . *Dactylis glomerata.*

    (c) Leaves very harsh ; all ribs very prominent ; densely tufted ; no distinct mid-rib *Deschampsia caespitosa.*

    (d) Sheath below ground yellow ; blade short, trough-shaped and leathery (may appear rolled in bud) ; ligule short ; dead flowering stems generally present . . . . *Cynosurus cristatus.*

(e) Short leaves with rough edges and low ribs ;
lower sheaths often reddish (poor pastures)
Briza media.

(f) Leaves rough, often rolled up ; alternate bands of
green and mealy white on sheath (roadsides)
Avena pratensis.

B. Leaf rolled in bud ; stem cylindrical.

(a) Vertical peglike projection opposite base of blade ; stem
square ; sheath hairy (woods)   .   . *Melica uniflora.*

(b) No peglike projection ; stem not square.

1. Claws at base of leaf.

(i) Sheath below ground smooth, shining pink ; ligule
very short.

(a) Margin of blade smooth ; veins indistinct (hold
up to light)   .   .   . *Lolium multiflorum.*

(b) Blade rougher, especially edges ; veins white
(hold up to light) ; ligule rim-like
Festuca pratensis.

(c) Leaves larger, harsher (woods) *Festuca gigantea.*

(d) Annual (cornfield weed)   . *Lolium temulentum.*
(*Agropyrum repens* may appear here also ; ligule
reduced to a rim.)

(ii) Sheath below ground not smooth and not shining pink.

(1) Basal sheaths distinctly hairy.

(a) Hairs long, prominent ; ligule prominent ; blade
large (woods)   . *Bromus asper and B. erectus.*

(b) Hairs short ; ligule very short ; blade thin, small
(pastures) .   .   .   . *Hordeum pratense.*

(c) Rim-like ligule   .   .   . *Agropyron repens.*

(2) Basal sheaths smooth or nearly so.

(a) Large seaside grass. Leaves thick, glaucous,
ridges prominent .   .   . *Elymus arenarius.*

(b) Markedly stoloniferous ; ligule a mere rim ; blade
shortly downy above (or occasionally smooth),

smooth below ; basal sheaths often redden in
dry positions   .   .   .   *Agropyron repens.*

(c) Ligule short ; blade thin, papery, downy above
and below (roadsides and waste places)
Hordeum murinum.

(d) Annual cornfield weed ; ligule very short
Lolium temulentum.

2. No claws at base of leaf.

(i) Lower sheaths hairy.

(1) A few long hairs around ligule, otherwise smooth ;
characteristic smell and taste
Anthoxanthum odoratum.

(2) Basal sheaths white with pink veins.

a. Tufted   .   .   .   .   . *Holcus lanatus.*

aa. Rhizomes   .   .   .   . *Holcus mollis.*

(3) Basal sheaths uniformly hairy and not with pink
veins.

†. Ligule prominent, membraneous.

A. Sheath keeled ; leaves thin, papery, hirsute.

(a) Leaves light green, covered with long hairs,
rather thinly scattered (woods)
Brachypodium sylvaticum.

(b) Leaves light green, slightly hairy ; rhizomes.
Brachypodium pinnatum.

(c) Leaves downy above and below ; hairs
short ; ribs indistinct (waste places and
cornfields)   .   .   . *Bromus mollis.*

(d) Leaves not so densely downy ; hairs longer ;
upper sheaths smooth (waste places) ; easily
develops red colour   .   . *Bromus sterilis.*

B. Sheath not keeled, leaves not papery, light
green   .   .   .   . *Trisetum flavescens.*

††. Ligule inconspicuous.

(a) Sheath and upper surface of blade sparsely

covered with long white hairs ; blade stiff
and pointed (moors)   .   *Molinia caerulea.*

(b) Sheath and blade hirsute ; blade narrow.
often inrolled ; ligule a yellow jagged line
(dry pastures) .   . .   *Koeleria cristata.*

(ii) Sheaths smooth or nearly so.

(1) Aquatics with large leaves.

(a) Ligule a tuft of hairs ; leaves 9″-18″ long, stiff,
ribs marked .   .   .   *Phragmites communis.*

(b) Ligule membraneous ; leaves smaller ; ribs low
Phalaris arundinacea.

(2) Plants not aquatic.

(*i*) Wood grass ; leaves large, light green, ligule
large   .   .   .   .   .   *Milium effusum.*

(*ii*) Meadow and pasture grasses.

A. Marked colour in old basal sheaths below ground.

(a) Sheath below ground dark brown, violet-
brown or nearly black ; blade large, markedly
ribbed   .   .   .   *Alopecurus pratensis.*

(b) Sheath below ground yellow (leaf really
folded in bud) ; dead flowering stems usually
present   .   . -   .   *Cynosurus cristatus.*

B. Old sheaths below ground not markedly coloured
(but Timothy often bright brown in outer old
sheaths).

(x) Leaf more or less prominently ribbed.

α. Perennial.

(a) Stem bent at nodes ; blade short, not keeled ;
sharply ribbed ; bluish-green (wet places)
Alopecurus geniculatus.

(b) Leaves very pointed and taped-based ; frequently has long stolons (cornfields, pastures,
waste places). Very short hairs on back of
ligule (hold to light and use lens). On drying, leaves become dark grey-green. Important distinctions from Phleum
Agrostis spp.

β. Annual cornfield weed ; upright tufts
Alopecurus myosuroides.

(xx) Ribs low and inconspicuous ; stem often swollen at base.

(a) Sheath prominently keeled ; leaves dark green with a bitter taste ; often sparsely hairy ; lower outer leaf bases often purple-red *Arrhenatherum elatius and A. bulbosum.*

(b) Sheath scarcely keeled, except at top ; leaves light green, sweet taste ; upright habit when young ; white at base ; ligule without hairs ; dries to silvery-grey colour ; often closely resembles A. grostis
Phleum pratense.

CHAPTER 4

BOTANICAL DESCRIPTIONS OF GRASSES

Agropyron repens (Couch Grass)

A. *Floral organs.*

Time of flowering—Mid and late summer.

Inflorescence—Spikate, erect, 2 to 6 inches long, culms 1 to 3 feet high.

Spikelets—Sessile on main axis, arranged on alternate sides ; 8 to 10 in number ; side of spikelet flat on rachis ; 4 to 6 flowers.

Glumes—Two, almost equal, narrow, stiff, pointed.

Pales—Two, outer one may or may not possess a short awn ; rachilla prominent.

Commercial seed—Single grain plus pales, plus rachilla.

B. *Vegetative organs.*

Habit of growth—Creeping perennial, with long stout rhizomes.

Root system—Fibrous, tufts of fibrous roots at nodes on rhizomes.

Shoots—Rounded.

Leaf sheath—Split, hairy, often red in dry places.

Leaf blade—Very pointed, downy above (or occasionally smooth), smooth below or slightly hairy ; slightly ribbed above.

Auricles—Prominent.

Ligule—Short, blunt.

C. *Distribution.*

Indigenous to Europe, Asia, America, and from Mediterranean to Arctic regions. Common in Britain on arable land.

D. *Economic value.*

A troublesome weed on most arable land.

FIG. 4.—A. Inflorescence. B. Spikelet. C. Commercial seed. D. Vegetative organs. E. Outline of leaf blade. F. Junction of leaf sheath and blade. G. Section through leaf blade.

18

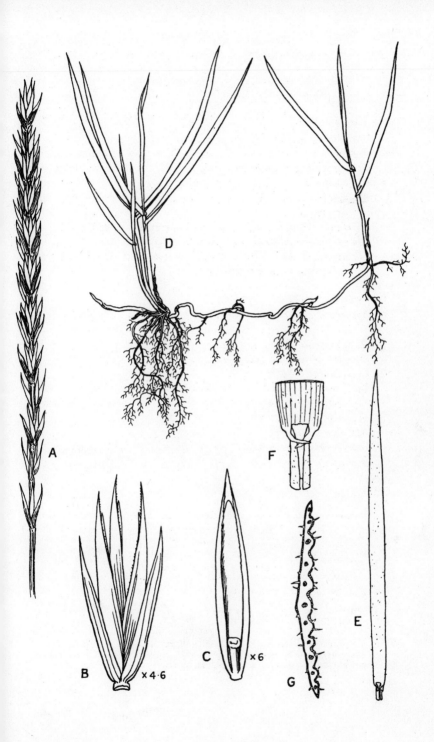

A

D

F

B ×4·6

C ×6

G

E

Agrostis tenuis (Brown top, or Common Bent)

A. *Floral organs.*

Time of flowering—Summer and early autumn.

Inflorescence—Panicle, erect, elegant, slender branches, spreading during time of flowering ; dark brown in colour when matured.

Spikelets—Numerous, small, one-flowered ; stalks vary in length.

Glumes—Two, almost equal in size, slightly keeled.

Pales—Two, awnless, a small tuft of hairs at base.

Commercial seed—Very small, composed of the two pales enclosing a small ovoid grain.

B. *Vegetative organs.*

Habit of growth—Varies from a dense tuft in dry places to a creeping perennial in richer soil.

Root system—Fibrous, fine, yellowish-brown.

Shoots—Rounded, glabrous.

Leaf sheath—Split.

Leaf blade—Rolled in the shoot, distinctly ribbed above ; long, narrow and finely pointed ; on drying becoming dark greyish-green.

Auricles—Absent.

Ligule—Short and blunt ; sometimes short hairs on back of ligule.

C. *Distribution.*

Indigenous to Europe, Asia and North America. Widely distributed in Britain. Most common on poor, dry, acid soils.

D. *Economic value.*

Nutritive value and palatability low. Productivity low. Not sown in seeds mixtures, except for the formation of lawns and greens. Creeping Bent or Fiorin is another common species grown extensively in Britain.

FIG. 5.—A. Inflorescence. B. Spikelet. C. Commercial seed. D. Vegetative organs. E. Outline of leaf blade. F. Junction of leaf sheath and blade. G. Section through leaf blade.

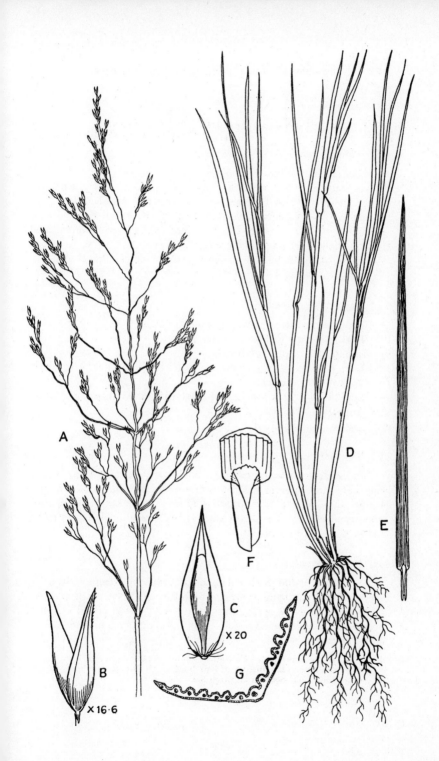

A

B

×16·6

C

×20

F

G

D

E

Alopecurus pratensis (*Meadow Foxtail*)

A. *Floral organs.*

Time of flowering—Spring and early summer.

Inflorescence—Cylindrical spike-like panicle, fairly compact and soft, 1 to 4 inches long ; culms 1 to 3 feet high.

Spikelets—Numerous, one-flowered, short stalks, flat.

Glumes—Two, equal length, boat-shaped, prominent keel with short hairs along edge.

Pales—Only outer one present, bearing slender basal awn.

Commercial seed—One complete spikelet.

B. *Vegetative organs.*

Habit of growth—Tufted perennial, slightly creeping.

Root system—Fibrous, yellow, sometimes short stolons.

Shoots—Rounded, glabrous.

Leaf sheath—Split, brown in colour, older ones very dark brown, glabrous.

Leaf blade—Dark green, large, flat, distinctly ribbed, glabrous.

Auricles—Absent.

Ligule—Small, blunt.

C. *Distribution.*

Indigenous to temperate and colder regions of Northern and Southern hemispheres. Most common in Britain on rich fertile heavy soils. Not to be confused with Slender Foxtail (*Alopecurus myosuroides*), which is also called Black Grass or Black Twitch, and is a weed of arable land.

D. *Economic value.*

Nutritive value and palatability extremely high. Productivity of some indigenous strains high throughout growing season. Very leafy in early spring and very winter green. Seed expensive and difficult to establish. Not normally recommended for seeds mixtures.

FIG. 6.—A. Inflorescence. B. Spikelet and commercial seed. D. Vegetative organs. E. Outline of leaf blade. F. Junction of leaf sheath and blade. G. Section through leaf blade.

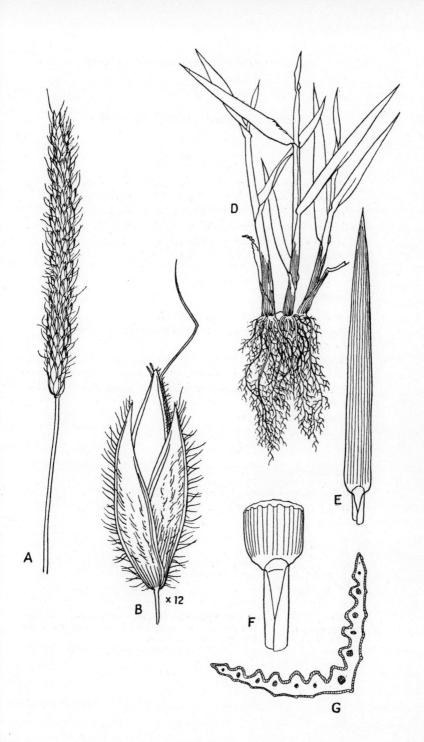

A

B   × 12

D

E

F

G

Ammophila arenaria (*Marram Grass*)

A. *Floral organs.*

Time of flowering—July.

Inflorescence—Panicle, erect, close, appearing as a cylindrical
spike, 5 to 6 inches long ; culms 1 to 3 feet high.

Spikelets—Crowded, long, narrow, containing one flower.

Glumes—Two, unequal, stiff.

Pales—Two, stiff, tuft of hairs on base.

Commercial seed—Single grain plus pales.

B. *Vegetative organs.*

Habit of growth—Creeping perennial.

Root system—Fibrous, rooting at nodes on rhizomes.

Shoots—Rounded.

Leaf sheath—Split.

Leaf blade—Rolled in shoot, erect, hard, narrow, usually
rolled, very pointed, prominent ribs on upper surface,
unequal, hairs on upper surface.

Auricles—Absent.

Ligule—Long, bifid.

C. *Distribution.*

Indigenous on coasts of Europe and North America.   Common
in Britain on sand dunes.

D. *Economic value.*

No agricultural value.   Used for sand binding, and mat
making.

Fig. 7.—A. Inflorescence.   B. Spikelet.   C. Commercial seed.   D. Vegetative organs.   E. Outline of leaf blade.   F. Junction of leaf sheath
and blade.   G. Section through leaf blade.

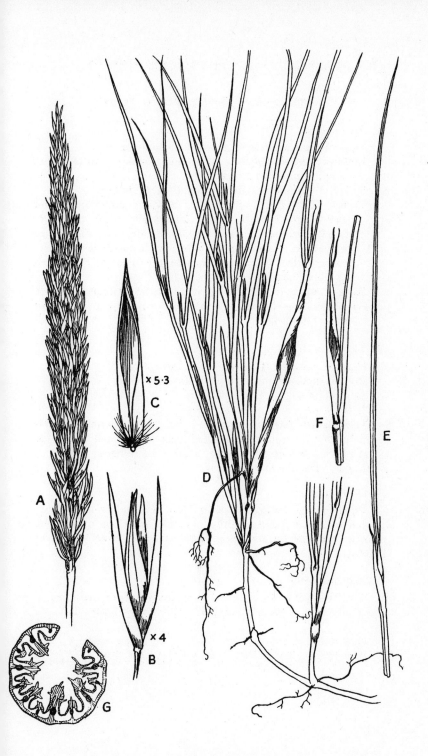

A

×5.3

C

×4

B

G

D

F

E

Anthoxanthum odoratum (Sweet Vernal)

A. *Floral organs.*

Time of flowering—Spring and early summer.

Inflorescence—Cylindrical spike-like panicle, 1 to 3 inches long ; culms 1 to 2 feet high.

Spikelets—Numerous, one-flowered, short stalks.

Glumes—Two pairs ; outer pair unequal, pointed but not awned, green when young but yellow when matured ; inner pair shorter than outer ones, hairy, and rich brown when ripe. Lower inner glume with small dorsal awn ; outer glume with basal awn longer than itself, twisted and bent near top of glume.

Pales—Two, brown, enclosing caryopsis ; two stamens per floret.

Commercial seed—Single grain, plus pales, plus innermost pair of glumes.

B. *Vegetative organs.*

Habit of growth—Tufted.

Root system—Fibrous, short, yellowish-brown.

Shoots—Rounded, often glabrous.

Leaf sheath—Split, slightly hairy.

Leaf blade—Fairly dark green, pointed, slightly hairy, faintly ribbed on upper surface ; characteristic smell and taste.

Auricles—Absent, replaced by small tufts of hairs.

Ligule—Prominent, white.

C. *Distribution.*

Indigenous to Europe, Asia and America, and, from Mediterranean to Arctic regions. Most common in Britain in southern counties. Found on all types of soil and in a great variety of habitats.

D. *Economic value.*

Nutritive value low, and not recommended for including in seeds mixtures. Strongly scented, but not very palatable.

Fig. 8.—A. Inflorescence. B. Spikelet. C. Commercial seed. C_1. Seed with inner glumes removed. D. Vegetative organs. E. Outline of leaf blade. F. Junction of leaf sheath and blade. G. Section through leaf blade.

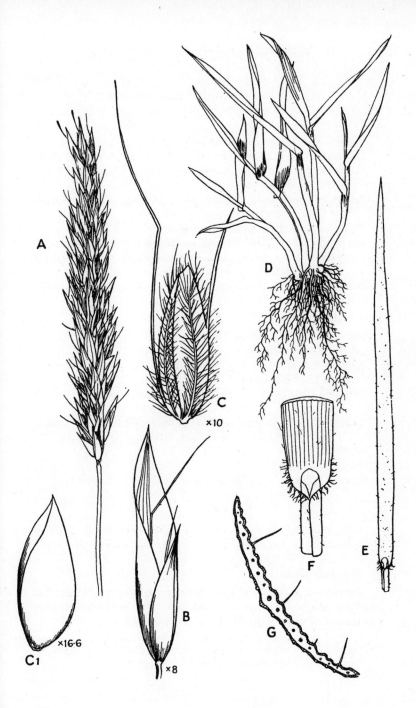

A

C
×10

C₁
×16·6

B
×8

D

E

F

G

3

Arrhenatherum elatius (Tall Oat Grass)

A. *Floral organs.*

Time of flowering—June and July.

Inflorescence—Panicle narrow, loose, 6 to 8 inches long ; spreading only when flowers are open ; culms 2 to 3 feet high.

Spikelets—Numerous, two flowers, the upper one perfect, the lower one staminate.

Glumes—Two, thin, pointed, unequal.

Pales—Two per floret ; dorsal, twisted and bent awn on outer pale of lower flower ; outer pale of upper flower possesses a minute sub-terminal awn ; hairs at base.

Commercial seed—Complete spikelet minus pair of glumes.

B. *Vegetative organs.*

Habit of growth—Loose, tufted perennial.

Root system—Fibrous, long, deep yellow.

Shoots—Rounded, older stems often with swollen nodes at base (A. bulbosum).

Leaf sheath—Split, sparsely hairy, older ones often purple red.

Leaf blade—Dark green, bitter taste, rolled in shoot, keeled, slightly hairy on upper surface, ribs on upper surface low ; long, narrow, pointed.

Auricles—Absent.

Ligule—Blunt ; variable in size.

C. *Distribution.*

Indigenous to Europe, Western Asia and North America. Most common in Britain in hedgerows and on light soils.

D. *Economic value.*

Proportion of leaf stem low. Cannot stand up to grazing, but produces heavy hay crop on light land. Its inclusion in seeds mixtures can only be justified under these conditions.

Fig. 9.—A. Inflorescence. B. Spikelet. C. Commercial seed. D. Vegetative organs. E. Outline of leaf blade. F. Junction of leaf sheath and blade. G. Section through leaf blade.

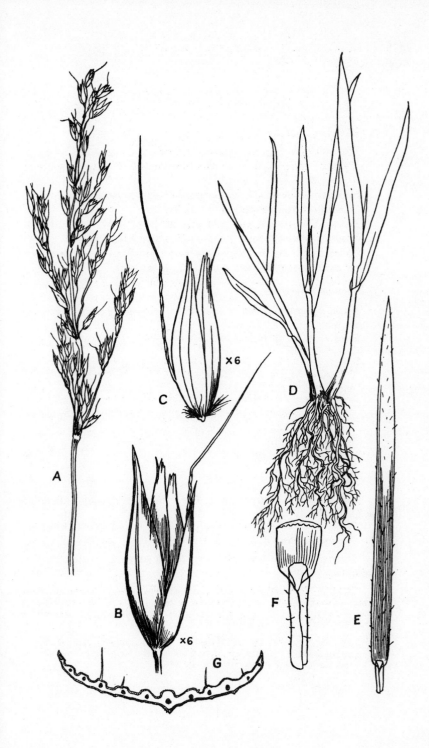

A

C

×6

D

B

×6

F

E

G

Avena pratensis (*Perennial Oat Grass*)

A. *Floral organs.*

Time of flowering—June and July.

Inflorescence—Panicle erect, almost reduced to a simple raceme ; 1 to 1½ feet high.

Spikelets—Erect, shining, large, 3 to 5 flowered.

Glumes—Two, unequal, pointed, keeled.

Pales—Two, outer one white, slightly cleft at apex, with a dorsal twisted awn ; awn bent, pales hairy at base.

Commercial seed—Single grain plus pales, plus rachilla ; rachilla round, long, hairy.

B. *Vegetative organs.*

Habit of growth—Erect perennial, sometimes slightly creeping.

Root system—Fibrous, yellowish-brown.

Shoots—Flat.

Leaf sheath—Split, usually glabrous, alternate bands of white and green.

Leaf blade—Folded in shoot; rough, often rolled up ; keeled below, almost ribless above ; glabrous. Sometimes slightly hairy.

Auricles—Absent.

Ligule—Fairly prominent.

C. *Distribution.*

Indigenous to Europe and Asia. Most common in Britain on Cotswolds.

D. *Economic value.*

Nutritive value low, used for rough grazing on dry, chalky soils.

There are two species of Wild Oat Grass that can be very troublesome weeds of arable land. These are Common or Spring Wild Oat (*Avena fatua*) and Winter Wild Oat (*Avena ludoviciana*). The Ministry of Agriculture Advisory leaflet No. 452, entitled *Wild Oats*, should be consulted.

Fig. 10.—A. Inflorescence. B. Spikelet. C. Commercial seed. D. Vegetative organs. E. Outline of leaf blade. F. Junction of leaf sheath and blade. G. Section through leaf blade.

A

F

D

C

×4·6

B

×3·3

G

E

Brachypodium pinnatum (*Heath False Brome Grass*)

A. *Floral organs.*

Time of flowering—June and July.
Inflorescence—Almost spikate, erect, culm 1 to 3 feet high.
Spikelets—Erect, long, 8 to 16 florets.
Glumes—Two, unequal, pointed, slightly hairy.
Pales—Two, outer pale with short terminal awn, slightly hairy.
Commercial seed—Single grain plus two pales, plus rachilla.

B. *Vegetable Organs.*

Habit of growth—Tufted perennial, creeping.
Root system—Fibrous, yellow.
Shoots—Rounded.
Leaf sheath—Split, hairy.
Leaf blade—Rolled in shoot, light green, stiff, erect, slightly hairy ; tendency to roll inwards.
Auricles—Absent.
Ligule—Long, prominent.

C. *Distribution.*

Indigenous to Europe and Asia. Most common in Britain in southern and eastern districts in broken down pastures.

D. *Economic value.*

Nutritive value low, not recommended for sowing in seeds mixtures.

Fig. 11.—A. Inflorescence. B. Spikelet. C. Commercial seed. D. Vegetative organs. E. Outline of leaf blade. F. Junction of leaf sheath and blade. G. Section through leaf blade.

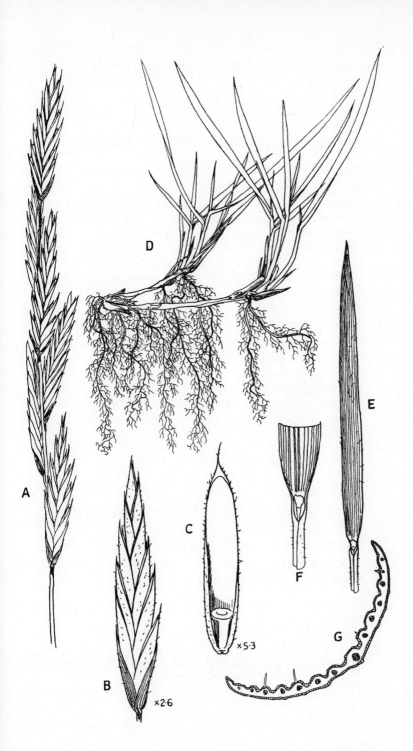

A

B   ×2·6

C   ×5·3

D

E

F

G

Brachypodium sylvaticum (*Wood False Brome Grass*)

A. *Floral organs.*

Time of flowering—June and July.

Inflorescence—Almost spikate, culms 1 to 3 feet high.

Spikelets—Long, almost drooping, about 1 inch long, 8 to 16 florets.

Glumes—Two, unequal, slightly hairy, pointed.

Pales—Two, outer one awned, inner one hairy along edges.

Commercial seed—Complete grain plus two pales, plus rachilla.

B. *Vegetative organs.*

Habit of growth—Tufted perennial, slightly creeping.

Root system—Fibrous, yellow.

Shoots—Rounded.

Leaf sheath—Split, hairy.

Leaf blade—Rolled in shoot, light green, long, very pointed, both surfaces sparsely covered with long hairs, slightly keeled below.

Auricles—Absent.

Ligule—Prominent, blunt, slightly serrated.

C. *Distribution.*

Indigenous to Europe and Asia, and most common in Britain in woods and shady places.

D. *Economic value.*

Nutritive value low, not sown in seeds mixtures.

FIG. 12.—A. Inflorescence. B. Spikelet. C. Commercial seed. D. Vegetative organs. E. Outline of leaf blade. F. Junction of leaf sheath and blade. G. Section through leaf blade.

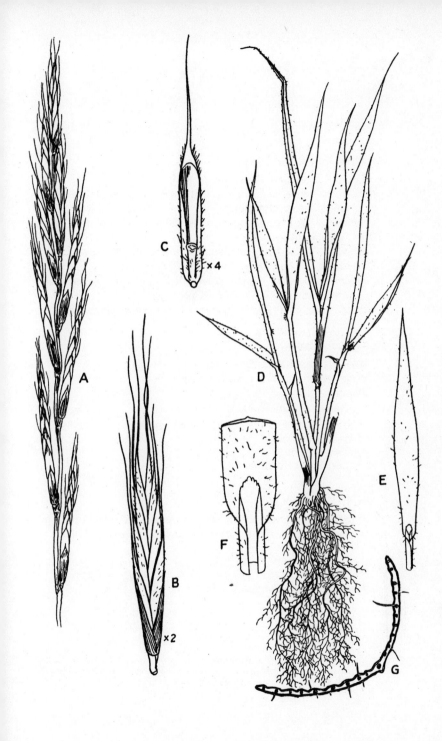

A

B ×2

C ×4

D

E

F

G

Bromus mollis (Soft Brome Grass)

A. *Floral organs.*

Time of flowering—May and June.

Inflorescence—Panicle erect, compact, 6 to 8 inches long ; culms 1 to 2 feet high.

Spikelets—Fairly numerous, 8 to 10 florets, broad at base, becoming pointed.

Glumes—Two, hairy, unequal ; outer glume reaching to about one-third way up spikelet.

Pales—Two, hairy ; outer pale broad, bifid apex, subterminal awn ; inner pale thin. Rachilla bent.

Commercial seed—One single grain plus pales, plus rachilla.

B. *Vegetative organs.*

Habit of growth—A tufted biennial, not very persistent.

Root system—Fibrous, yellowish-brown.

Shoots—Rounded.

Leaf sheath—Entire, hairy, striated.

Leaf blade—Hairy above and below ; pointed, ribs almost indistinct.

Auricles—Absent.

Ligule—Short, serrated.

C. *Distribution.*

Indigenous to Europe and Asia. Common in Britain in open waste places and cornfields, often in hayland on sandy soils.

D. *Economic value.*

Nutritive value and palatability low.

FIG. 13.—A. Inflorescence. B. Spikelet. C. Commercial seed. D. Vegetative organs. E. Outline of leaf blade. F. Junction of leaf sheath and blade. G. Section through leaf blade

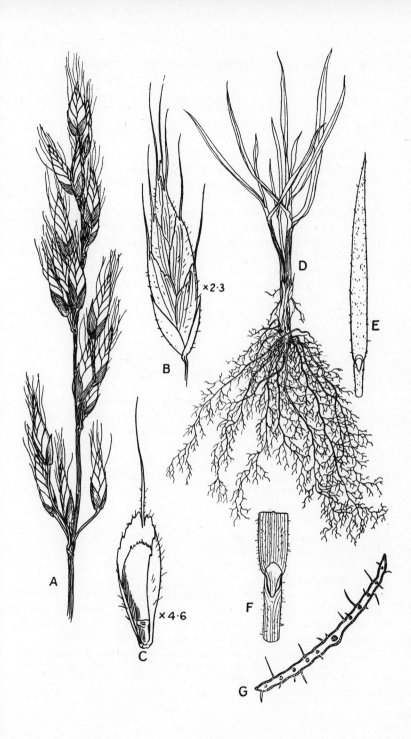

A

B   ×2·3

C   ×4·6

D

E

F

G

Cynosurus cristatus (Crested Dogstail)

A. *Floral organs.*

Time of flowering—June and July.

Inflorescence—One-sided spikelike panicle, erect, 1 to 3 inches long ; culm stiff, wiry when old, approximately 1 foot high.

Spikelets—Numerous, in almost sessile clusters arranged on one side of the axis ; the outer spikelet of the cluster sterile, the inner one fertile containing 3 to 5 florets.

Glumes—Two per spikelet, equal in size in both empty and flowering spikelets ; keeled, short awn, pointed.

Pales—Two, usually a bright yellow colour, especially towards the base ; rachilla cylindrical, prominent, capped.

Commercial seed—Single grain plus pales, plus rachilla.

B. *Vegetative organs.*

Habit of growth—Dense, tufted perennial.

Root system—Fibrous, yellowish-brown.

Shoots—Rounded, glabrous.

Leaf sheath—Split, yellow below ground when old, glabrous.

Leaf blade—Rolled in shoot, dark green, short, leathery ; trough-shaped near base, ribbed above, glossy below, glabrous.

Auricles—Absent.

Ligule—Very short, blunt.

C. *Distribution.*

Indigenous to Europe, Asia and America. Common on poor dry soils, and also on rich soils.

D. *Economic value.*

Nutritive value and palatability high. Productivity highest during late summer. Rapidly develops wiry flowering stems, which are unattractive to stock. Very winter green and valuable as a bottom grass on upland pastures and poor dry soils.

Fig. 14.—A. Inflorescence. B. Fertile spikelet. B₁. Sterile spikelet. C. Commercial seed. D. Vegetative organs. E. Outline of leaf blade. F. Junction of leaf sheath and blade. G. Section through leaf blade.

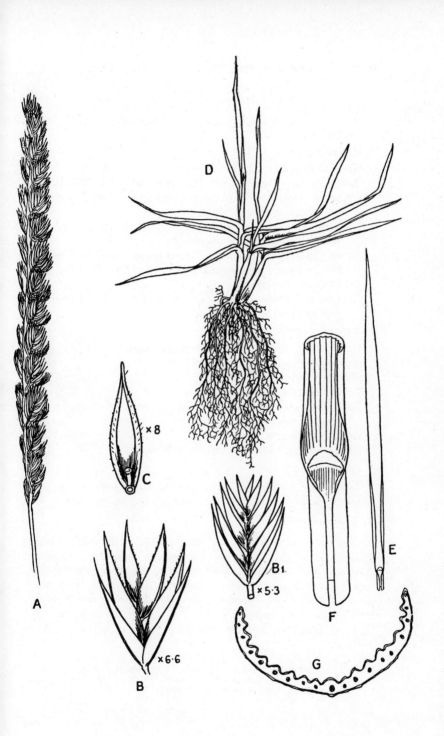

A

C ×8

B ×6·6

B₁ ×5·3

D

E

F

G

Dactylis glomerata (*Cocksfoot*)

A. *Floral organs.*

Time of flowering—May and June.

Inflorescence—Panicle erect, flowering stalks 2 to 3 feet high.

Spikelets—Arranged in dense clusters on short stiff branches, 2 to 3 flowers per spikelet.

Glumes—Two glumes almost equal, distinctly keeled and pointed, rough edges, slightly hairy.

Pales—Two, outer pale with curved point keeled from top to bottom, inner one membranous ; rachilla cylindrical and prominent, capped.

Commercial seed—Consists of grain plus pales, frequently two or three seeds attached.

B. *Vegetative organs.*

Habit of growth—Densely tufted perennial.

Root system—Fibrous, yellowish-brown.

Shoots—Flat.

Leaf sheath—Entire, glabrous, keeled.

Leaf blade—Folded in shoot, light green, glabrous, rough edges, ribless above, keeled below ; pointed.

Auricles—Absent.

Ligule—Long, membraneous, conspicuous.

C. *Distribution.*

Indigenous to Europe, Asia and Africa. Most common in Britain on heavy, fertile soils in meadows and waste places.

D. *Economic value.*

Nutritive value high, and very palatable in young stage. Productivity high. Starts growth early in spring, and recovers quickly in the aftermath. Recommended for seeds mixtures for both temporary and permanent pastures. Pedigree leafy varieties are available to suit different purposes. The prostrate varieties are suitable for grazing, and the taller leafy varieties for hay. There are also intermediate varieties.

FIG. 15.—A. Inflorescence. B. Spikelet. C. Commercial seed. D. Vegetative organs. E. Outline of leaf blade. F. Junction of leaf sheath and blade. G. Section through leaf blade.

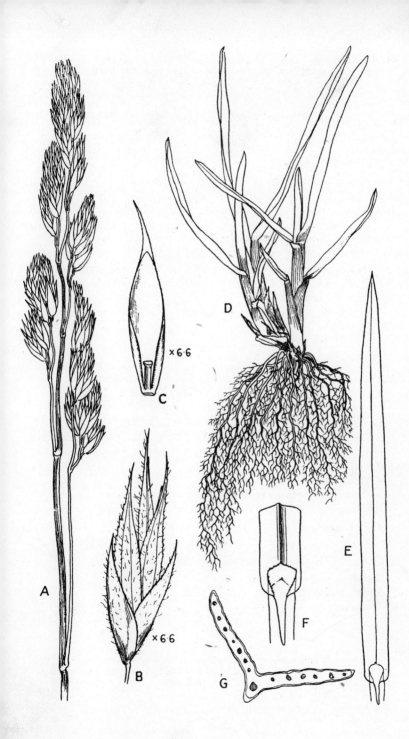

A

C ×6·6

B ×6·6

D

E

F

G

Deschampsia caespitosa (*Tufted Hair Grass*)

A. *Floral organs.*

Time of flowering—July and August.

Inflorescence—Panicle, spreading slender branches, some-times 1 foot long ; culms 2 to 4 feet high.

Spikelets—Numerous, 2 to 3 flowers per spikelet ; purplish or silvery-grey in colour.

Glumes—Two, unequal, long and pointed.

Pales—Two, outer pale serrated at apex with fine awn in-serted near its base ; not so long as the pale itself ; tuft of hairs at base.

Commercial seed—Single grain plus pale, plus rachilla. Rachilla long, hairy.

B. *Vegetative organs.*

Habit of growth—A tall densely, tufted perennial.

Root system—Very fibrous, yellowish-brown.

Shoots—Rounded, glabrous.

Leaf sheath—Split, slightly keeled, glabrous.

Leaf blade—Dark green, very harsh, ribs on upper surface equal and very prominent ; no distinct mid-rib, pointed ; glabrous.

Auricles—Absent.

Ligule—Long, whitish, acute.

C. *Distribution.*

Indigenous to Europe, and from Mediterranean to Arctic regions. Common in Britain in moist, shady places.

D. *Economic value.*

Nutritive value low, a weed in wet shady places. Very un-palatable.

Fig. 16.—A. Inflorescence. B. Spikelet. C. Commercial seed. D. Vege-tative organs. E. Outline of leaf blade. F. Junction of leaf sheath and blade. G. Section through leaf blade.

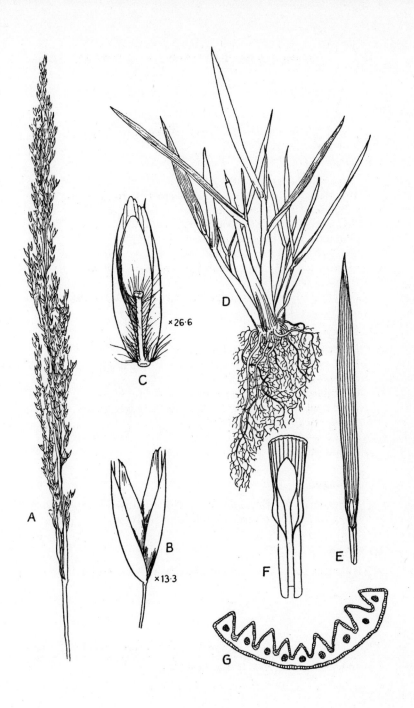

A

C ×26·6

B ×13·3

D

E

F

G

4

Deschampsia flexuosa (*Wavy Hair Grass*)

A. *Floral organs.*

Time of flowering—July.

Inflorescence—Spreading panicle erect, 2 to 3 inches long ; culms 1 to 1½ feet high.

Spikelets—Numerous, two flowers, shiny.

Glumes—Two, unequal, pointed.

Pales—Two, outer one notched at apex with basal awn ; awn twisted, longer than pale and bent half-way ; minute hairs near base.

Commercial seed—Single grain plus pales, plus rachilla.

B. *Vegetative organs.*

Habit of growth—Tufted perennial.

Root system—Very fibrous, reddish in colour.

Shoots—Rounded, glabrous.

Leaf sheath—Split, glabrous.

Leaf blade—Dark green, needle-like ; edges rolled inwards, practically solid, glabrous.

Auricles—Absent.

Ligule—Short, broad.

C. *Distribution.*

Indigenous to Europe, Asia, North America and Chile. Common in Britain on heaths and hilly pastures.

D. *Economic value.*

Nutritive value low and not sown in seeds mixtures.

Fig. 17.—A. Inflorescence. B. Spikelet. C. Commercial seed. D. Vegetative organs. E. Outline of leaf blade. F. Junction of leaf sheath and blade. G. Section through leaf blade.

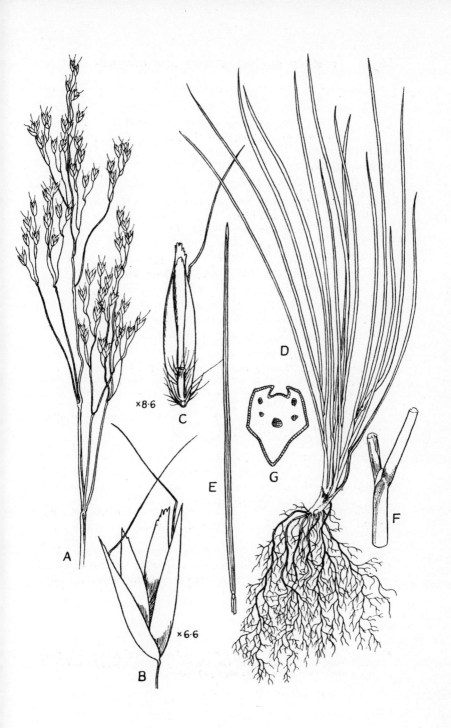

×8·6

C

×6·6

B

A

D

E

G

F

Festuca ovina (Sheep's Fescue)

A. *Floral organs.*

Time of flowering—May and June.

Inflorescence—Panicle compact, 2 to 4 inches long, culms 1 to 2 feet high.

Spikelets—5 to 8 florets.

Glumes—Two, unequal, slightly hairy.

Pales—Two, outer pale glabrous or hairy, short awn point ; rachilla round, prominent.

Commercial seed—Complete grain plus pales, plus rachilla.

B. *Vegetative organs.*

Habit of growth—Tufted perennial, dense.

Root system—Very fibrous, yellowish-brown.

Shoots—Cylindrical.

Leaf sheath—Split.

Leaf blade—Folded in shoot, dark green, radical leaves, permanently folded, needle-like, glabrous, delicate, stem leaves open and flat.

Auricles—Small, erect.

Ligule—Very small, often absent.

C. *Distribution.*

Indigenous to Europe, Asia, North America, and from Mediterranean to the Arctic regions. Most common in Britain in hilly pastures and in open dry places.

D. *Economic value.*

Nutritive value and palatability moderately high. Productivity low. Hardy and drought resistant. Useful grass on poor upland pastures. Not usually recommended for inclusion in seeds mixtures.

FIG. 18.—A. Inflorescence. B. Spikelet. C. Commercial seed. D. Vegetative organs. E. Outline of leaf blade. F. Junction of leaf sheath and blade. G. Section through leaf blade.

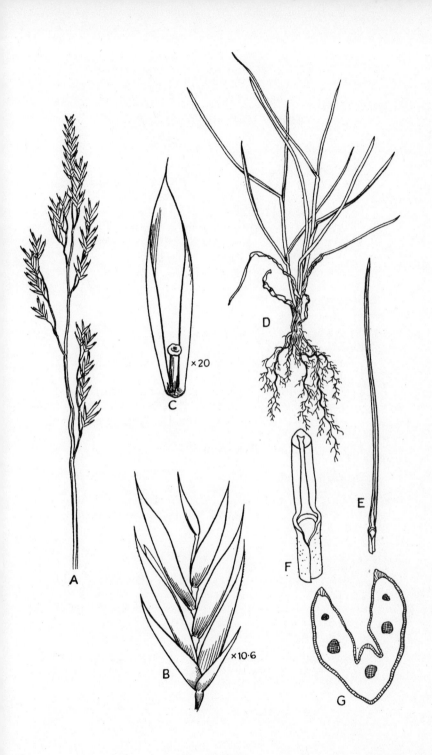

A

C ×20

D

B ×10·6

F

E

G

Festuca pratensis (*Meadow Fescue*)

A. *Floral organs.*

Time of flowering—June and July.

Inflorescence—Panicle, with secondary branches large ; culms 1 to 2 feet high.

Spikelets—5 to 10 flowers.

Glumes—Two, unequal, outer one large and pointed.

Pales—Two, outer pale slightly awned or very pointed ; rachilla cylindrical, capped, outstanding.

Commercial seed—One single grain, plus pales and rachilla.

B. *Vegetative organs.*

Habit of growth—Tufted perennial.

Root system—Fibrous, yellowish-brown.

Shoots—Rounded.

Leaf sheath—Split, reddish colour around basal parts ; glabrous.

Leaf blade—Rolled in shoot, dark green, distinct ribs above, lower surface smooth, glossy ; keeled ; edges harsh when old ; distinct white longitudinal lines when held to light.

Auricles—Small if present.

Ligule—Small, rim-like, blunt.

C. *Distribution.*

Indigenous to Europe, Asia and North America. Most common in Britain on rich, heavy, moist pastures, especially when soil is rich in lime.

D. *Economic value.*

Nutritive value high. Very palatable when young and leafy. High proportion of leaf to stem. Recommended in seeds mixtures for leys, along with suitable varieties of Timothy and White Clover. Tall Fescue is similar, but coarser; and varieties have recently been evolved to produce very early grazing.

FIG. 19.—A. Inflorescence. B. Spikelet. C. Commercial seed. D. Vegetative organs. E. Outline of leaf blade. F. Junction of leaf sheath and blade. G. Section through leaf blade.

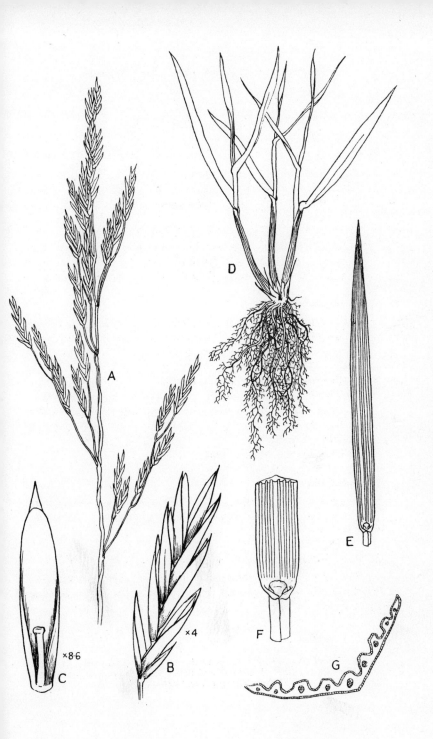

A

D

×8·6

C

×4

B

F

E

G

Festuca rubra (Red Fescue)

A. *Floral organs.*

Time of flowering—June and July.

Inflorescence—Panicle, compact, 2 to 4 inches long, culms 1 to 2 feet high ; erect, reddish when ripe.

Spikelets—5 to 8 florets.

Glumes—Two, unequal, may be slightly hairy.

Pales—Two, outer pale usually red ; awn point short but may vary in length ; rachilla round.

Commercial seed—One single grain plus pales and rachilla.

B. *Vegetative organs.*

Habit of growth—Tufted perennial, may sometimes be slightly creeping.

Root system—Fibrous, yellowish-brown.

Shoots—Rounded to oval.

Leaf sheath—Mostly entire, sometimes slightly hairy.

Leaf blade—Folded in shoot ; dark green ; stem leaves flat, other leaves mostly folded and needlelike. Usually a few scattered hairs.

Auricles—Small.

Ligule—Minute, often absent.

C. *Distribution.*

Indigenous to Europe, Asia, North America, and from Mediterranean to Arctic regions. Most common in Britain in hilly pastures.

D. *Economic value.*

Nutritive value and palatability improved in the new varieties, which remain winter green. Particularly useful for re-seeding upland pastures.

Fig. 20.—A. Inflorescence. B. Spikelet. C. Commercial seed. D. Vegetative organs. E. Outline of leaf blade. F. Junction of leaf sheath and blade. G. Section through leaf blade.

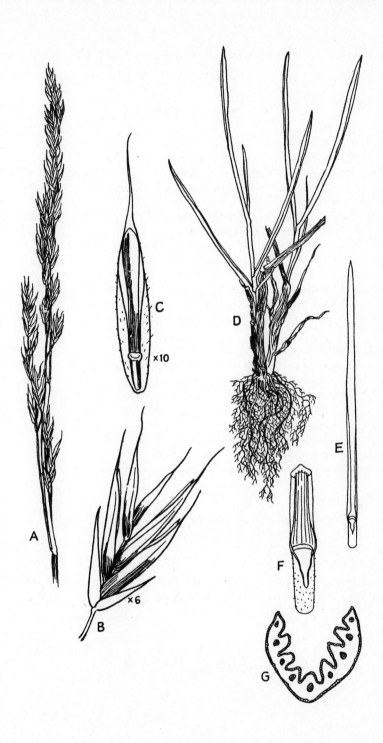

A

C

×10

D

E

B

×6

F

G

Holcus lanatus (*Yorkshire Fog*)

A. *Floral organs.*

Time of flowering—June and July.

Inflorescence—Panicle, 2 to 3 inches long ; close green and compact when young, open and spreading later ; pinkish in colour.

Spikelets—Numerous, two flowers ; the lower flower perfect, the upper one staminate.

Glumes—Two, hairy, unequal, the outer one broad with a short awn point ; keeled.

Pales—Two, outer pale of lower flower awnless, shiny, and the outer pale of the upper flower with a sub-terminal fish hook awn, becoming curved when older.

Commercial seed—Usually the complete spikelet.

B. *Vegetative organs.*

Habit of growth—Tufted, sometimes slightly creeping.

Root system—Yellowish-brown.

Shoots—Round.

Leaf sheath—Split, hairy ; basal sheaths white with pink longitudinal veins.

Leaf blade—Lightish-green, hairy, rolled in shoot.

Auricles—Absent.

Ligule—Prominent, serrated, membraneous, hairy.

C. *Distribution.*

Indigenous to Europe and Asia. Most common in Britain in moist meadows and waste places.

D. *Economic value.*

Palatability low, indigenous strains sometimes recommended for seeds mixtures for improving upland pastures; but regarded as a weed grass in lowland pastures.

Fig. 21.—A. Inflorescence. B. Spikelet. C₁. Upper and lower florets. D. Vegetative organs. E. Outline of leaf blade. F. Junction of leaf sheath and blade. G. Section through leaf blade.

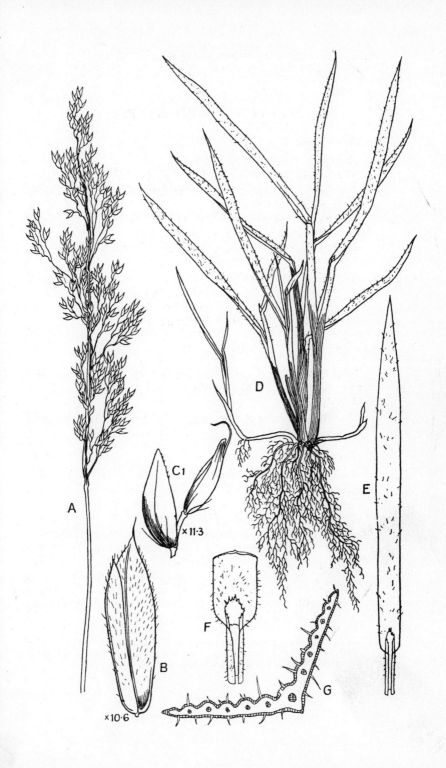

A

C₁

× 11·3

B

× 10·6

D

F

G

E

Lolium multiflorum (Italian Rye-grass)

A. Floral organs.

Time of flowering—May or June.

Inflorescence—Spikate, erect, 1 to 2 feet high.

Spikelets—3 to 10 florets, alternating in two rows on rachis, edge on to rachis.

Glumes—Inner glume absent ; outer glume shorter than spikelet.

Pales—Outer pale smooth, with distinct terminal awn.

Commercial seed—Single grain plus pales, plus rachilla. Rachilla flat to rounded.

B. Vegetative organs.

Habit of growth—Tufted, dense.

Root system—Fibrous, yellowish-brown.

Shoots—Rounded, glabrous.

Leaf sheath—Split, reddish colour below, glabrous.

Leaf blade—Dark green, margin smooth, glossy below, dull above, distinctly ribbed ; blades rolled in shoot, glabrous.

Auricles—Prominent when old.

Ligule—Small, blunt.

C. Distribution.

Cultivated strains in temperate regions. Not indigenous to Britain.

D. Economic value.

Nutritive value and palatability high. Productivity high during spring and autumn months. Persists for two years only. Sown in seeds mixtures for temporary leys. Useful for early spring bite and catch cropping. Sometimes used as a nurse crop in direct re-seeding. There are several varieties on the market. H.1 Rye-grass is derived from a cross between Italian and Perennial Rye-grass, and used for short leys.

FIG. 22.—A. Inflorescence. B. Spikelet. C. Commercial seed. D. Vegetative organs. E. Outline of leaf blade. F. Junction of leaf sheath and blade. G. Section through leaf blade.

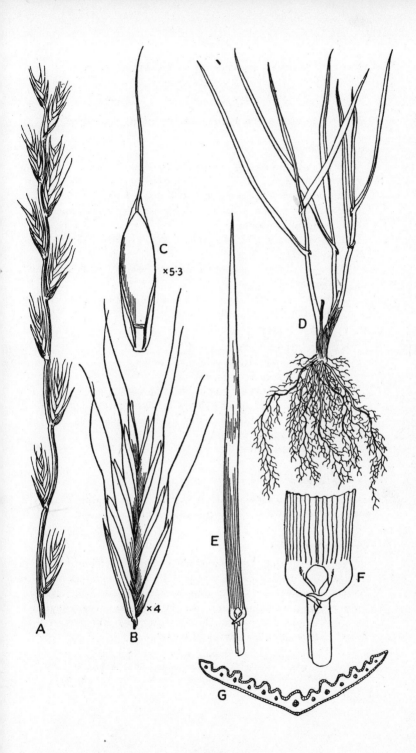

A

C

×5·3

B

×4

D

E

F

G

Lolium perenne (*Perennial Rye-grass*)

A. *Floral organs.*

Time of flowering—June, with considerable variation according to strain and other factors.

Inflorescence—Spikate, erect, 1 to 2 feet high.

Spikelets—Sessile 3 to 10 florets, alternating in two rows, edge on to rachis.

Glumes—Inner glume absent; outer glume shorter than spikelet.

Pales—Outer pale smooth; awnless, rachilla oval in section. No cap.

Commercial seed—Single grain plus pales. Barge shape, rachilla flat, elliptical in section.

B. *Vegetative organs.*

Habit of growth—Tufted.

Root system—Fibrous, yellowish-brown.

Shoots—Flattened, glabrous.

Leaf sheath—Entire or split, reddish colour below, glabrous.

Leaf blade—Dark green, glossy below, dull above, distinctly ribbed. Leaf blades folded in shoot; glabrous.

Auricles—Small if present.

Ligule—Small, blunt.

C. *Distribution.*

Indigenous to fertile soils in Britain, Europe and Asia. Uncommon on moorlands and upland pastures.

D. *Economic value.*

Nutritive value and palatability high. Productivity high throughout growing season and persists over a number of years. Both commercial and indigenous strains sown in seeds mixtures for permanent and temporary leys. Pedigree strains are available to suit different purposes, such as grazing, hay and intermediate types. There are also tetraploid varieties.

Fig. 23.—A. Inflorescence. B. Spikelet. C. Commercial seed. D. Vegetative organs. E. Outline of leaf blade. F. Junction of leaf sheath and blade. G. Section through leaf blade.

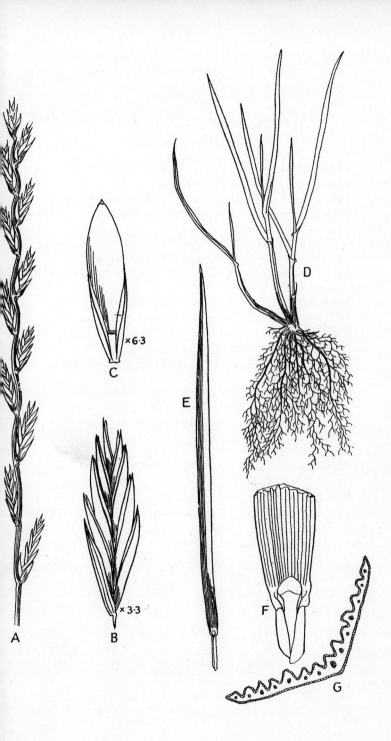

A   B   ×3·3   C   ×6·3   D   E   F   G

Molinia caerulea (*Flying Bent*)

A. *Floral organs.*

Time of flowering—July and August.

Inflorescence—Panicle narrow, 6 inches long, green to purplish, branches arise in alternate tufts on the culm; culm swollen at base.

Spikelets—Numerous, small, narrow, pointed, 2 to 3 flowers.

Glumes—Two, unequal, acute, shorter than pales.

Pales—Two, purple, open at top; rachilla rounded, swollen near tip.

Commercial seed—Single grain plus pales, plus rachilla.

B. *Vegetative organs.*

Habit of growth—Stiff coarse perennial tufts.

Root system—Fibrous, tough, cord-like, yellowish-brown.

Shoots—Rounded.

Leaf sheath—Split, slightly hairy.

Leaf blade—Long, narrow, flat, stiff; rolled in shoot, very pointed; upper surface sparseley covered with long white hairs.

Auricles—Absent.

Ligule—Inconspicuous, represented by presence of hairs.

C. *Distribution.*

Indigenous to Europe and Asia, and from Mediterranean to Arctic regions. Most common in Britain on wet heaths, upland moors, woods and waste places.

D. *Economic value.*

Nutritive value, low, not sown in seeds mixtures.

Fig. 24.—A. Inflorescence. B. Spikelet. C. Commercial seed. D. Vegetative organs. E. Outline of leaf blade. F. Junction of leaf sheath and blade. G. Section through leaf blade.

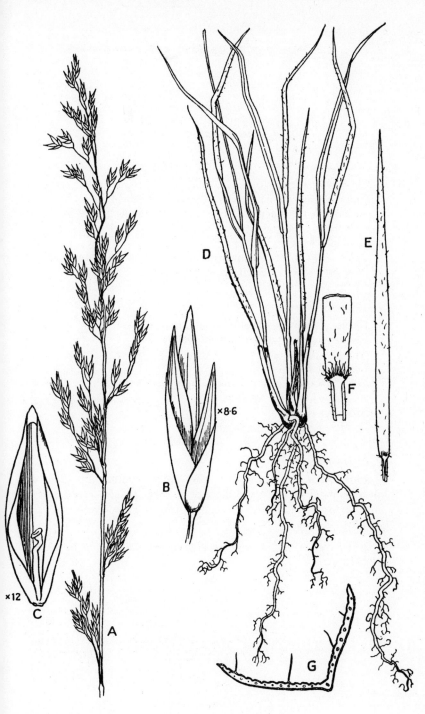

×8·6

×12

A

B

C

D

E

F

G

5

Nardus stricta (*Moor Mat Grass*)

A. *Floral organs.*

Time of flowering—July.

Inflorescence—Spike, erect, culms 1 to 2 feet high.

Spikelets—Arranged on one side of rachis ; sessile, one flowered ; often purplish in colour.

Glumes—Absent.

Pales—Two, outer one narrow and ending in a fine awn point.

Commercial seed—Single grain plus pales.

B. *Vegetative organs.*

Habit of growth—Dense, tufted perennial.

Root system—Tough and wiry, yellowish.

Shoots—Round.

Leaf sheath—Split.

Leaf blade—Hard, glaucous, upright, permanently folded, 5 ribs, on upper surface.

Auricles—Absent.

Ligule—Small and blunt, thick.

C. *Distribution.*

Indigenous to Europe and Asia. Most common in Britain on dry upland pastures and moors.

D. *Economic value.*

Nutritive value low, not recommended for sowing in seeds mixtures.

FIG. 25.—A. Inflorescence. B. Spikelet. C. Commercial seed. D. Vegetative organs. E. Outline of leaf blade. F. Junction of leaf sheath and blade. G. Section through leaf blade.

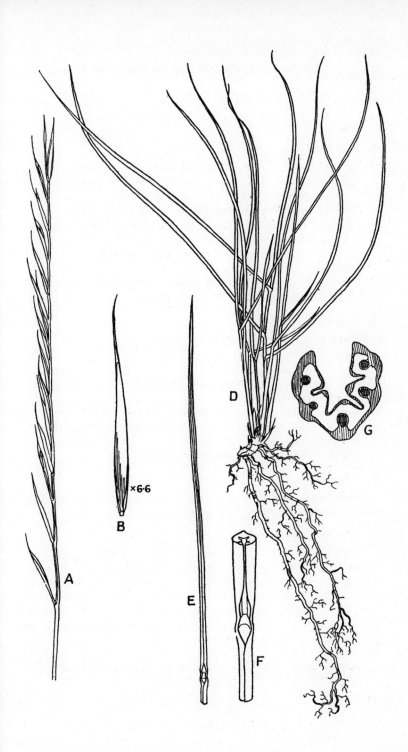

A B ×6·6 D E F G

Phleum pratense (*Timothy*)

A. *Floral organs.*

Time of flowering—July and August.

Inflorescence—Cylindrical compact spike-like panicle, 1 to 6 inches long ; culms 1 to 2½ feet high.

Spikelets—Numerous, one-flowered, very short stalks.

Glumes—Two, equal length, broad, slightly hairy ; keeled, terminating in rough awn points ; awns shorter than glumes ; short stiff hairs along edges of keel.

Pales—Two, thin, silvery-white.

Commercial seed—Ovoid in shape, silvery-white ; one complete spikelet minus two outer glumes.

B. *Vegetative organs.*

Habit of growth—Tufted perennial.

Root system—Fibrous, yellowish-white.

Shoots—Rounded, glabrous, older shoots swollen at base.

Leaf sheath—Glabrous, split, brown in colour when old, slightly keeled.

Leaf blade—Light green, slightly keeled, blades rolled in shoot, sweet taste ; dries to silvery-grey colour, glabrous.

Auricles—Absent.

Ligule—White, membranous, prominent.

C. *Distribution.*

Indigenous to Europe and Asia. Abundant in Britain, and thrives best on low-lying, heavy soils.

D. *Economic value.*

Nutritive value and palatability high. Commercial varieties stemmy. Indigenous leafy varieties are available to suit different purposes. For grazing there are very prostrate, spreading types. For hay, tall very leafy types. There are also intermediate types. Timothy produces very heavy hay crops on good soil. Sown in seeds mixtures both temporary and permanent, especially on heavy soil with Meadow Fescue and White Clover.

FIG. 26.—A. Inflorescence. B. Spikelet. C. Commercial seed. D. Vegetative organs. E. Outline of leaf blade. F. Junction of leaf sheath and blade. G. Section through leaf blade.

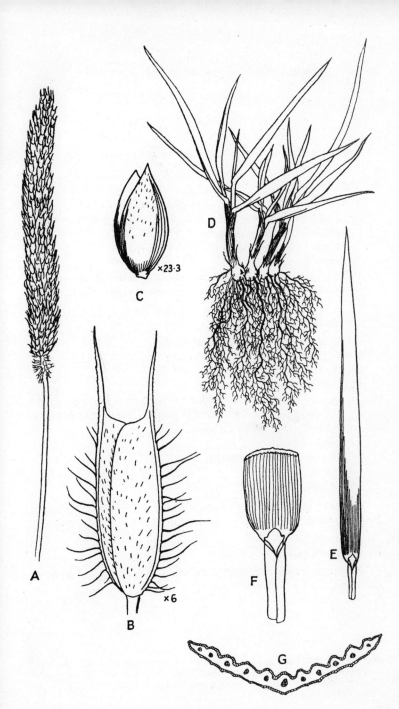

A

×23·3

C

D

B

×6

F

E

G

Poa annua (*Annual Meadow Grass*)

A. *Floral organs.*

Time of flowering—Almost throughout whole year.

Inflorescence—Panicle 1 to 3 inches long, loose, spreading culms 3 to 12 inches high.

Spikelets—Oblong to ovate, 3 to 6 flowered.

Glumes—Two, unequal.

Pales—Two, outer pale with minute silky hairs along keel.

Commercial seed—Single grain plus pales, plus rachilla.

B. *Vegetative organs.*

Habit of growth—Small, tufted annual.

Root system—Yellowish-brown, fibrous.

Shoots—Flat.

Leaf sheath—Split, glabrous.

Leaf blade—Light green, folded in shoot, blunt apex ; upper surface dull with two faint tram-like lines running longitudinally from apex to base ; glabrous.

Auricles—Absent.

Ligule—Long, membraneous.

C. *Distribution.*

Common in almost every part of the globe.   Most common in Britain as a weed in gardens, parks and waste places.

D. *Economic value.*

Nutritive value low, not recommended for sowing in seeds mixtures.

FIG. 27.—A. Inflorescence.   B. Spikelet.   C. Commercial seed.   D. Vegetative organs.   E. Outline of leaf blade.   F. Junction of leaf sheath and blade.   G. Section through leaf blade.

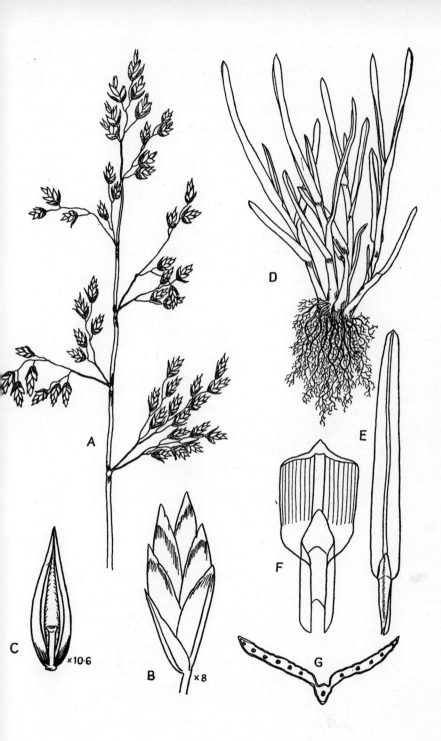

A

B   ×8

C   ×10·6

D

E

F

G

Poa pratensis (Smooth-stalked Meadow Grass)

A. *Floral organs.*

Time of flowering—May and June.
Inflorescence—Panicle erect, spreading at time of flowering ;
culms 1 to 2 feet high.
Spikelets—Ovate, 3 to 5 flowered.
Glumes—Two, unequal, keeled.
Pales—Two, upper one not pointed ; hairs along bottom
half of keel ; conspicuous web of hairs at base.
Commercial seed—Single grain plus pales, plus rachilla.

B. *Vegetative organs.*

Habit of growth—Creeping perennial (rhizomes).
Root system—Fibrous, tuft of roots at nodes of rhizomes.
Shoots—Flat.
Leaf sheath—Entire, glabrous, smooth.
Leaf blade—Dark green, folded in shoot, blunt apex, upper
surface dull ; two longitudinal lines from apex to base ;
keeled below, glabrous.
Auricles—Absent.
Ligule—Small throughout.

C. *Distribution.*

Indigenous to Europe, Asia and North America, and from
Mediterranean to Arctic circle. Common in Britain in rich, damp
meadows and pastures, also in dry hedgerows.

D. *Economic value.*

Nutritive value and palatability high. Sometimes recommended for sowing in seeds mixtures as a bottom grass in open,
rich soils, and for hard-wearing lawns. Popular in parts of North
America, where it is known as Kentucky Blue Grass.

FIG. 28.—A. Inflorescence. B. Spikelet. C. Commercial seed. D. Vegetative organs. E. Outline of leaf blade. F. Junction of leaf sheath
and blade. G. Section through leaf blade.

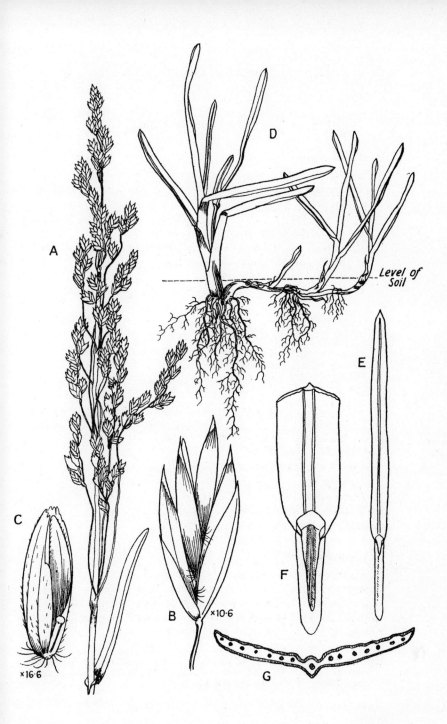

A

C
×16·6

B
×10·6

D

Level of
Soil

E

F

G

Poa trivialis (*Rough-stalked Meadow Grass*)

A. Floral organs.

Time of flowering—July and August.

Inflorescence—Panicle erect, about 6 inches long with slender spreading branches; culms 1 to 3 feet high.

Spikelets—Numerous, 2 to 5 flowers, usually two, seldom more than three, ovate, short stalks.

Glumes—Two, outer glume slightly longer than inner one; keeled, minute hairs along keel.

Pales—Two, outer pale pointed; web of hairs at base.

Commercial seed—Single grain plus pales, plus rachilla.

B. Vegetative organs.

Habit of growth—Loose spreading tufts.

Root system—Fibrous, small tufts at nodes on stolons.

Shoots—Flat, glabrous.

Leaf sheath—Not split, minute asperites on old sheath, glabrous.

Leaf blade—Dark green, shining below, keeled, apex pointed, hooded tip. Two tramline-like lines from apex to base; glabrous.

Auricles—Absent.

Ligule—Short on lower leaves, long on upper ones.

C. Distribution.

Indigenous to Europe, Central Asia and America. Most common in Britain on rich, moist, heavy soils.

D. Economic value.

Nutritive value and palatability high. Not very productive. Persistent on account of its creeping habit. Sown in seeds mixtures for permanent pastures as a bottom grass on rich, moist soil, but inclined to suppress the more valuable species in a wet season.

FIG. 29.—A. Inflorescence. B. Spikelet. C. Commercial seed. D. Vegetative organs. E. Outline of leaf blade. F. Junction of leaf sheath and blade. G. Section through leaf blade.

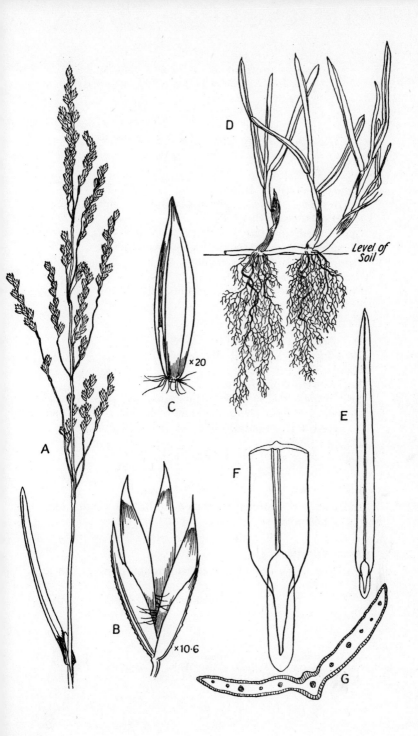

Level of
Soil

A

B ×10·6

C ×20

D

E

F

G

Sieglingia decumbens (*Mountain Heath Grass*)

A. *Floral organs.*

Time of flowering—July.

Inflorescence—Panicle contracted into a simple raceme ; culms about 1 foot high.

Spikelets—Comparatively few in a panicle, 3 or 4 flowered.

Glumes—Two, equal, pointed, glabrous, keeled.

Pales—Two, outer one rounded on back, ending in three points ; a tuft of hairs at its base.

Commercial seed—Single grain plus pales, plus rachilla.

B. *Vegetative organs.*

Habit of growth—Tufted perennial.

Root system—Yellowish, fibrous, long.

Shoots—Flat.

Leaf sheath—Split, hairy.

Leaf blade—Folded in shoot, long, narrow, pointed, usually long, soft hairs along edges and underside ; ribless above, except for two parallel lines on each side of midrib.

Auricles—Absent.

Ligule—Represented by a tuft of hairs.

C. *Distribution.*

Indigenous to Europe. Common in Britain on dry heaths and hilly pastures.

D. *Economic value.*

Nutritive value low; but useful for rough grazing on heaths and hilly pastures.

FIG. 30.—A. Inflorescence. B. Spikelet. C. Commercial seed. D. Vegetative organs. E. Outline of leaf blade. F. Junction of leaf sheath and blade. G. Section through leaf blade.

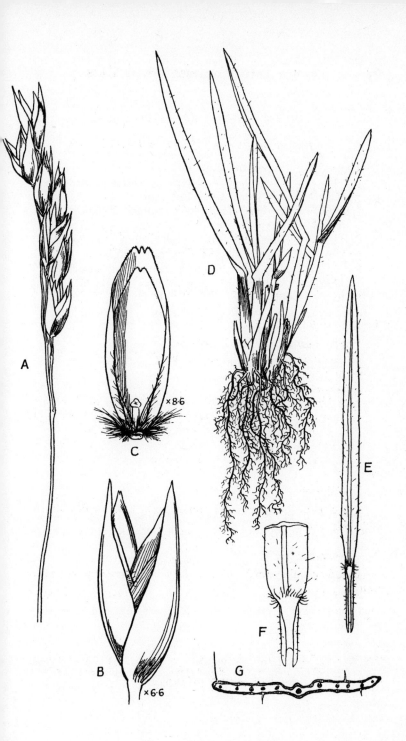

A

B ×6·6

C ×8·6

D

E

F

G

Trisetum flavescens (Golden Oat Grass)

A. *Floral organs.*

Time of flowering—June and July.

Inflorescence—Panicle erect, slender, spreading branches, 3 to 5 inches long ; culms 1 to 2 feet high.

Spikelets—Numerous, small, erect, shining, yellowish, 2 to 3 flowers.

Glumes—Two, unequal, upper or inner glume approximatel three times as large as the lower one ; thin, pointed.

Pales—Two, outer pale with dorsal awn ; awn twisted, bent ; bifid apex ; inner pale thin, awnless ; tufts of hairs at base ; rachilla hairy.

Commercial seed—Single grain plus pales, plus rachilla.

B. *Vegetative organs.*

Habit of growth—Tufted perennial, erect.

Root system—Fibrous, yellow.

Shoots—Rounded.

Leaf sheath—Split, hairy.

Leaf blade—Light green ; hairs on both surfaces, hairs reflexed, ribbed above.

Auricles—Absent.

Ligule—Prominent.

C. *Distribution.*

Indigenous to Europe, Asia, Scandinavia and America. Most common in Britain on heavy soils containing a fair amount of lime.

D. *Economic value.*

Nutritive value and palatability high. Productivity low. High proportion of stem to leaf. Not usually recommended for seeds mixtures.

FIG. 31.—A. Inflorescence. B. Spikelet. C. Commercial seed. D. Vegetative organs. E. Outline of leaf blade. F. Junction of leaf sheath and blade. G. Section through leaf blade.

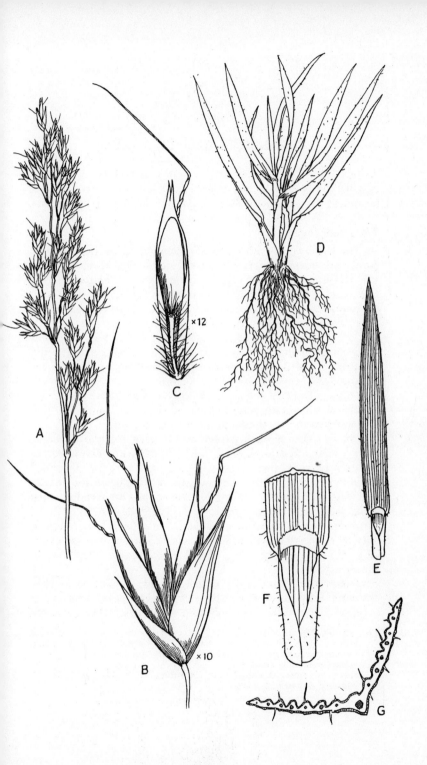

A

C

×12

D

E

B

×10

F

G

CHAPTER 5

LEGUMINOSAE (CLOVER FAMILY)

As in the section on grasses the morphological features of Leguminous plants may be conveniently studied under two separate headings : (*a*) the Floral Organs, and (*b*) the Vegetative Organs.

The Floral Organs.

The flowers of clovers and other members of the Leguminosae family are usually brightly coloured, and arranged on a central axis to form a racemose type of inflorescence. The form of the inflorescence varies in different species ; in Red Clover the flowers are grouped together at the end of a main stem, whereas in Lucerne they arise in the axils of the leaves.

A single flower (Fig. 32 A) is often described as papilionaceous on account of its close resemblance to the common butterfly, and consists of 5 sepals (calyx), 5 petals (corolla), 10 stamens (androecium), and 1 carpel (gynaecium).

Calyx.—The five sepals are usually joined together to form a tube at the base, with the tip of each remaining free and appearing as five tooth-like projections (Fig. 32 B).

Corolla.—The petals are coloured and very irregular in shape, with a characteristic claw at the base of each. The upper or posterior petal is broad and conspicuous, and is commonly called the standard (Fig. 32 c). The two side or wing petals are usually free (Fig. 32 D), whilst the two lowermost ones are usually joined along their outer edges to form the keel (Fig. 32 E).

Androecium.—The filaments of the ten stamens (male organs) may be either all united to form a sheath surrounding the ovary (Fig. 32 F) or the upper one free and the other nine joined to form the sheath.

Gynaecium.—The single carpel (female organ) is usually surrounded by the stamens (Fig. 32 F). The ovary (Fig. 32 G) is one-celled, containing one or more ovules (Fig. 32 H), arranged

FIG. 32.—A. Flower of Gorse. B. Calyx. C. Standard petal. D. Wing petals. E. Keel petals. F. Stamens. G. Carpel. H. Longitudinal section through carpel. J. Fruit or pod. K. Mature pod split to release seed. L. Seed.
1. Bract ; 2. claws ; 3. sheath ; 4. filaments ; 5. anthers ; 6. style ; 7. stigma ; 8. ovules ; 9. seed.

74

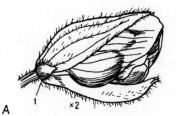

A

1   ×2

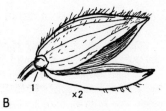

B

1   ×2

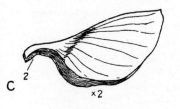

C

2   ×2

D

2   ×2

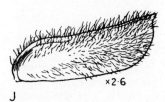

E

2   ×2

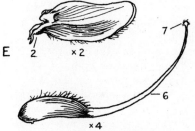

F

5   6   7

4

3   ×4 6

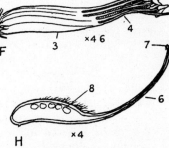

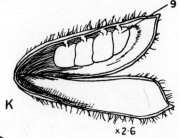

G

7

6

×4

H

7

8

6

×4

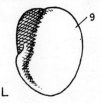

J

×2·6

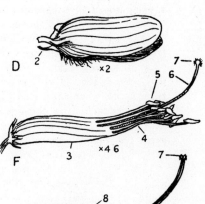

K

9

×2·6

L

9

along the upper edge of the cavity. The style varies in length in the different species and is terminated by a sticky stigma

Fertilisation.—The flowers of clovers are usually self-sterile, and cross-pollination is carried out by insects and bees, which seek the honey glands at the base of the stamens. When the insects alight on the wing petals, the keel is automatically depressed, causing the emergence of the stigma and stamens. The visiting insect then becomes dusted with pollen, which is in turn transferred to another flower of the same type.

The Fruit.—After fertilisation the ovary develops into a fruit which, in the majority of cases, is termed a legume or pod (Fig. 32 J). It varies in shape and size according to the species ; in Lucerne (Fig. 39 F) it is spirally twisted and contains two or three seeds, whereas in Red Clover it takes the form of an ovoid one-seeded structure commonly called a pyxidium (Fig. 47 F). The pod may split along both edges to release the seed with great force as in Bird's-foot Trefoil, or along one side only as in Wild White Clover and Gorse (Fig. 32 K).

The Seed.—The seeds are usually round to oval in shape with a firm leathery seed-coat (Fig. 32 L). A scar or hilum is often visible on the seed-coat where it was once joined to the ovary wall (Fig. 33 G), and near this may be seen a minute hole called the micropyle, which connects with the interior of the seed. Within the seed coat are two seed-leaves or cotyledons, in between which lie the radicle and plumule (Fig. 32 H). Upon germination these develop into a root and shoot respectively (Fig. 33 J).

Germination.

With an adequate supply of water, air and temperature the seeds begin to germinate. The cotyledons, which usually appear above the ground, supply the young developing embryo with reserved food material. The portion between the radicle and the cotyledons (Fig. 33 D) is called the hypocotyl, and in clovers this grows more rapidly than the epicotyl, which lies between the plumule and the cotyledons (Fig. 33 E). In the Vetch the

FIG. 33.—A. Seed of Red Clover.   B. Seed-coat removed.   C. First stage in germination (epigeal).   D. Second stage in germination.   E. Third stage in germination.   F. Fourth stage in germination.   G. Seed of Vetch.   H. Seed-coat and one cotyledon removed.   J. First stage in germination (hypogeal).   K. Second stage in germination.
1. Seed-coat ;   2. cotyledons ;   3. radicle ;   4. hypocotyl ;   5. plumule ;   6. first leaf ;   7. second leaf ;   8. hilum ;   9. epicotyl.

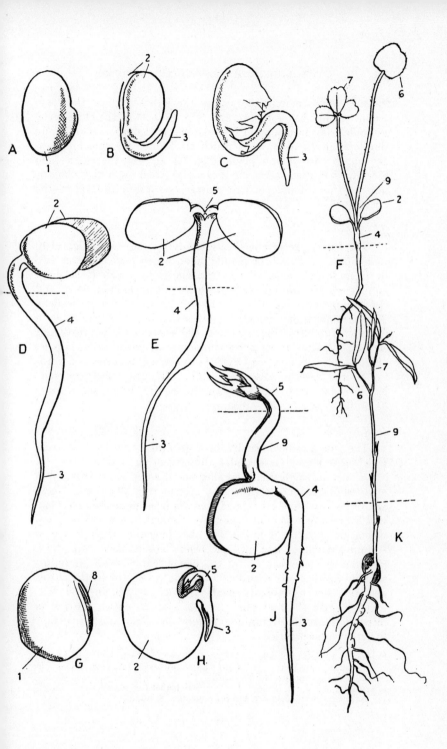

epicotyl grows more rapidly than the hypocotyl and the cotyledons remain below the ground (Fig. 33 J).   In the clovers the
plumule arises from a point between the cotyledons, and gradually
develops into a stem, upon which are formed the first and sub-
sequent leaves of the plant (Fig. 33 F).   At the same time
secondary rootlets arise on the radicle, and soon the plant is
able to lead an independent existence, without the aid of the
cotyledons.

The Leaves.

The leaves are arranged alternately on the stem (Fig. 36 B)
and consist of a stalk or petiole, upon which may be borne two
or more leaflets according to the family to which it belongs ;
e.g. the clovers are trifoliate, with three leaflets (Fig. 34 B) and
Sainfoin pinnate (Fig. 34 D), with several pairs of opposite leaflets.
The terminal leaflet sometimes takes the form of a tendril as in
Meadow Vetchling (Fig. 34 A).   At the base of each leaf stalk may
be found a pair of appendages common to all clovers called stipules
(Fig. 34 B) and which may differ in shape, size and colour according to the species.   These, together with other features, such
as mucronate tips (Fig. 34 C), hairiness and colour, often serve
as useful guides for identification purposes.

Root System.

The young radicle usually develops into a long tap root from
which arise numerous secondary branches (Fig. 35 B).
Numerous small swellings called nodules appear, distributed in
an irregular manner on the root system (Fig. 34 E, F).   These
are formed by a special type of bacteria (species of *Pseudomonas*)
which find their way into the plant through the root hairs, and
which are capable of fixing and absorbing into their system a
certain amount of free nitrogen from the air in the soil.   This
nitrogen is made use of by the clover plant which in return
supplies the bacteria with food material.   As a result, the clover
and all other leguminous plants are rich in protein, and this,
together with the fact that the root systems enrich the soil in
nitrogen, make the leguminous family one of the most important
in agricultural practice.

Fig. 34.—A. Leaf of Meadow Vetchling. B. Leaf of Red Clover. C. Leaf of
    Lucerne.   D. Leaf of Sainfoin.   E. Nodules on roots of Sainfoin.   F.
    Nodules on roots of Red Clover.
1. Tendril ; 2. lateral leaflets ; 4. stipules ; 5. mucro-
    nate tip ; 6. petiole ; 7. lateral rootlets ; 8. nodules.

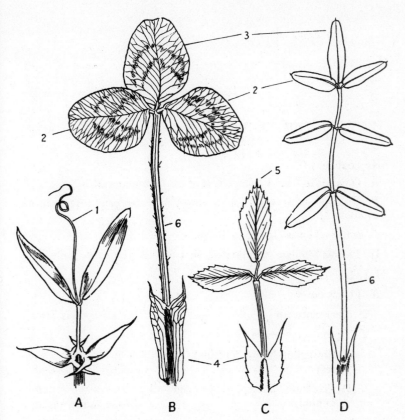

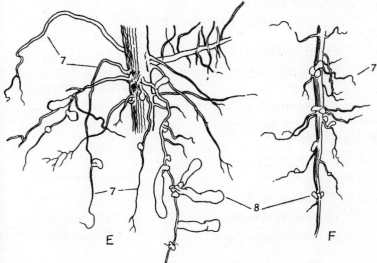

A   B   C   D

E   F

CHAPTER 6

KEY TO THE VEGETATIVE CHARACTERS OF SOME COMMON LEGUMES

I. Leaf simple.

A. Obcordate—First foliage leaf of *Trifolium* and *Medicago*.

B. Oblong—Lowest leaves of *Anthyllis vulneraria* (upper ones compound).

C. Spiny—Lowest leaves of *Gorse*.

II. Leaves bifoliate, terminating in a tendril   *Lathyrus pratensis*.

III. Leaves trifoliate.

A. Plants hairy.

  1. Mucronate tip .   .   .   .   . *Medicago lupulina*.

  2. Tip not mucronate.

    (*a*) Straggling habit, terminal leaflet at a distance from the rest .   .   .   .   .   . *Trifolium dubium*.

    (*b*) Prostrate habit, pubescence silky, leaves obcordate, annual .   .   .   . *Trifolium subterraneum*.

    (*c*) Upright habit.

      (i) Stipules blunt, with purple border at apex

                           Trifolium incarnatum.

      (ii) Stipules pointed.

        α. Stipules adherent to petiole, frequently with red lines .   .   .   .   . *Trifolium pratense*.

        β. Stipules free from petiole, narrow and pointed; stems zig-zagging .   .   . *Trifolium medium*.

B. Plants hairless.

  1. Tip not mucronate.

    (*a*) Upright habit .   .   .   . *Trifolium hybridum*.

    (*b*) Straggling habit.

      (i) Rooting at nodes .   .   . *Trifolium repens*.

      (ii) Not rooting at nodes .   .   . *Trifolium dubium*.

2. Tip mucronate ; edge coarsely serrated round apex only
Medicago sativa.

IV. Leaves pentafoliate.

Three terminal leaflets and one pair of stipule-like leaflets at base
Lotus corniculatus.

V. Leaflets more than five.

A. Terminal leaflet present.

    1. Terminal leaflet no longer than others.

       (*a*) Softly nairy with lowest pair close to the stem
Ornithopus perpusillus.

       (*b*) Glabrous above, slightly downy underneath ; stipules
pointed, brown or pink . . . *Onobrychis sativa.*

    2. Terminal leaflet longer than others *Anthyllis vulneraria.*

B. Terminal leaflet replaced by tendril.

    1. Tip mucronate, dark spot on stipule, stipule toothed
Vicia sativa.

    2. Tip not mucronate.

       (*a*) Four to six pairs leaflets . . . *Vicia sepium.*

       (*b*) About ten pairs leaflets . . . . *Vicia cracca.*

CHAPTER 7

BOTANICAL DESCRIPTIONS OF LEGUMINOSAE FAMILY

Anthyllis vulneraria (Kidney Vetch)

A. *Floral organs.*

Time of flowering—July.

Inflorescence—Flower heads usually in pairs at the ends of the stems, each one subtended by a divided bract.

Flowers—Numerous on short stalks ; calyx 5, inflated, hairy, narrow at the mouth ; petals 5, yellow to red, small ; stamens all united ; ovary with 2 ovules ; stalked.

Fruit—Flat pod, black, one-seeded.

Seed—Oval, 2·5 mm. long, green at base and yellow near apex ; smooth.

B. *Vegetative organs.*

Seedling—Cotyledons above ground ; first leaf simple, long, slightly hairy.

Habit of growth—Tufted perennial.

Stems—Erect, and mostly produced in second year, 12 to 18 inches long, slightly hairy.

Leaves—During first year mostly simple, forming rosette, later pinnate with large terminal leaflets ; which spring from axil of simple leaves, slightly hairy ; stipules small, ledge-like.

Root system—Tap root long, numerous secondary roots ; nodules large.

C. *Distribution.*

Indigenous to Europe and Western Asia, and from Mediterranean to Arctic regions. Most common in Britain in dry pastures on calcareous soils.

D. *Economic value.*

Sown in drills, or broadcast alone, on dry poor calcareous soils (20 lb. per acre) for sheep grazing. It may be sown also in permanent seeds mixtures on such soils, usually with sainfoin.

Fig. 35.—A. Seedling. B. Complete plant. C. Leaf. D. Inflorescence. E. Floret. F. Fruit. G. Seed.

82

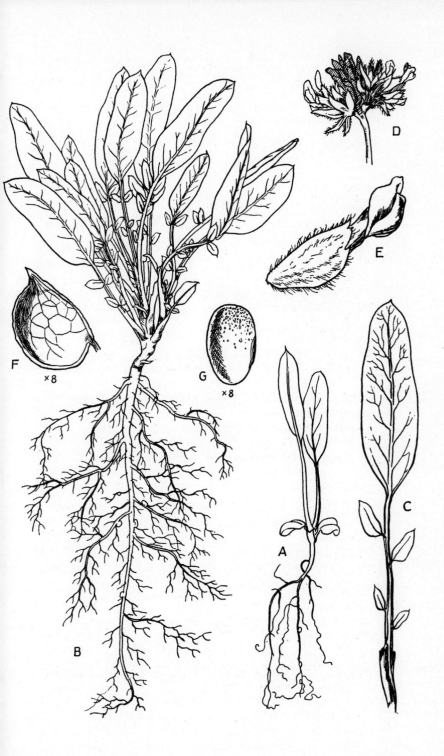

F ×8

G ×8

A

B

C

D

E

Lathyrus pratensis (Meadow Vetchling)

A. *Floral organs.*

Time of flowering—June and July.

Inflorescence—Short raceme of 6 to 10 flowers, on end of long stalks.

Flowers—Prominent, calyx 5, sharply pointed, hairy ; petals 5, yellow, standard broad ; stamens 10, upper one free ; ovary containing several ovules ; style flat.

Fruit—Pod almost glabrous, seeds several.

Seed—Globular, dark brown.

B. *Vegetative organs.*

Seedling—Cotyledons remain below ground ; first leaf with one pair leaflets, and one pair sharply pointed stipules, no tendrils.

Habit of growth—Straggling to half-climbing perennial.

Stems—1 to 2 feet long, weak, straggly.

Leaves—One pair leaflets, short stalk ; leaflets linear ; tendrils ; stipules pointed, prominent teeth at base.

Root system—Slender tap root, numerous branches.

C. *Distribution.*

Indigenous to Europe and Asia. Abundant in Britain in moist meadows and hedgerows.

D. *Economic value.*

On account of a low production of leaf, the plant is not cultivated, but it is sometimes eaten by cattle in the wild state.

FIG. 36.—A. Seedling. B. Complete plant. C. Leaf. D. Inflorescence. E. Floret. F. Fruit. G. Seed.

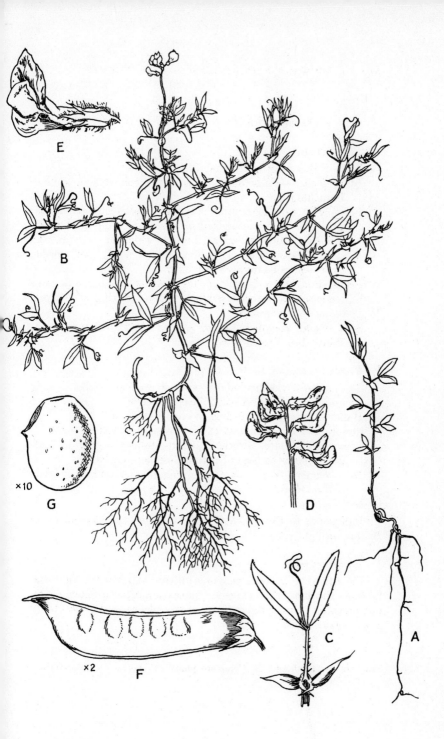

×10

G

×2   F

A

B

C

D

E

Lotus corniculatus (*Bird's-foot Trefoil*)

A. *Floral organs.*

Time of flowering—June and July.

Inflorescence—Umbel-like cymes at the end of long axillary branches.

Flowers—4 to 6 in number ; calyx 5, teeth not spreading ; petals 5, yellow, standard often tinged red ; keel petals joined, tubular at apex, through which the stigma and pollen emerge when pollinated by bees ; self-sterile ; ovary contains numerous ovules.

Fruit—Pod about 1 to 2 inches long, containing numerous seeds which are released by sudden splitting of the pod along both edges.

Seed—Small rounded, kidney shaped, 1·5 to 2 mm. long ; shiny, dark brown or chocolate.

B. *Vegetative organs.*

Seedling—Cotyledons above ground, short stalks ; long epicotyl ; first and second leaves trifoliate.

Habit of growth—Spreading to erect perennial.

Stems—Numerous, about 12 inches long, sometimes hairy.

Leaves—Trifoliate, alternate, short stalks ; a pair of leaf-like stipules at base of petiole ; sometimes hairy.

Root system—Tap root, long, numerous secondary rootlets and nodules.

C. *Distribution.*

Indigenous to Europe, Asia and Australia. Most common in Britain on light soils.

D. *Economic value.*

Usually sown in seeds mixtures on land which is too light and poor. to support other clovers. Lotus major, distinguished by its spreading calyx, prefers damp shady places, and is profitably sown on such soils.

Fig. 37.—A. Seedling. B. Complete plant. C. Leaf. D. Inflorescence. F. Fruit. G. Seed.

A

B

C

D

F

×·6

G
×16·6

Medicago lupulina (*Trefoil, Black Medick, Hop Clover*)

A. *Floral organs.*

Time of flowering—July.

Inflorescence—Compact raceme, oval in shape, borne at the ends of long axillary branches.

Florets—Bright yellow, small, numerous ; calyx 5, equal ; petals 5, standard petal large ; ovary containing one ovule ; after fertilisation the ovary becomes twisted and black.

Fruit—Pod, one-seeded, small, slightly hairy, curved almost into complete ring.

Seed—Plump, greenish-yellow, shining, 2 mm. long ; definite projection where radicle ends.

B. *Vegetative organs.*

Seedling—Cotyledons above ground, almost round, short stalks ; first leaf simple with a distinct projecting mid-rib (mucronate tip), slightly hairy.

Habit of growth—Annual, stem spreading, sub-erect.

Stems—1 to 2 feet long, hairy.

Leaves—Trifoliate, leaflets sometimes hairy with long stalk to terminal one : ovate in shape with projecting mid-rib (mucronate tip) ; stipules serrated and very pointed.

Root system—Tap root, long ; numerous nodules.

C. *Distribution.*

Indigenous to Europe and Asia. Most common in Britain on calcareous soils.

D. *Economic value.*

Not recommended in seeds mixtures except in small quantities for temporary leys on dry, chalky soil. It is sometimes sown on such soils with corn crops, to plough in later with the stubble as a green manure ; or for silage after potatoes.

FIG. 38.—A. Seedling. B. Complete plant. C. Leaf. D. Inflorescence. E. Floret. F. Fruit. G. Seed.

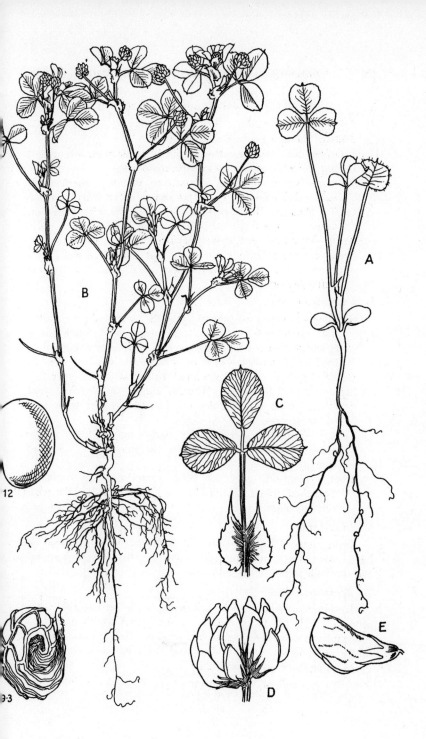

Medicago sativa (Alfalfa, Lucerne)

A. Floral organs.

Time of flowering—July and August.

Inflorescence—Close raceme, borne on axillary stalks, spreading from the axils of leaves on main stem.

Flowers—Violet to blue, sometimes yellow ; short stalks subtended by small bracts at base ; calyx 5 teeth, petals 5 ; stamens 10, upper one free ; ovary with numerous ovules ; cross-fertilised by bees.

Fruit—Dehiscent pod, spirally twisted, several seeds.

Seed—Irregular, kidney shape to oval ; point of radicle not prominent ; usually bent appearance, 2 to 3 mm. long, yellowish-brown.

B. Vegetative organs.

Seedling—Cotyledons above ground, with short stalks ; first leaf simple, glabrous (mucronate tip) ; internode of epicotyl elongated bearing second leaf, presenting a long seedling, not rosette as in most other clovers.

Habit of growth—Erect perennial, tufted after first year.

Stems—1 to 2 feet long, glabrous, numerous in second year, arising from lower nodes of older stems and from axils of cotyledons.

Leaves—Trifoliate, short stalks ; leaflets may be hairy, upper margin serrated ; mucronate tip; stipules broad, serrated, sharply pointed.

Root system—Usually tap root, sometimes tap roots are branched giving out aerial roots ; numerous nodules when soil inoculated.

C. Distribution.

Indigenous to Europe, Asia and America. When the seed has been inoculated, the plant grows well in Britain on deep calcareous soils in the south and east.

D. Economic value.

Recommended for sowing alone in drills on suitable soils ; seeding, 15 to 20 lb. per acre. Usually cut green or fed off. Known to produce five cuts in one season. Used in manufacture of Lucerne meal. Deep rooted and drought resistant. Many varieties are now on the market.

FIG. 39.—A. Seedling. B. Complete plant. C. Leaf. D. Inflorescence E. Floret. F_1. Collection of fruits. F_2. Single fruit. G. Seed.

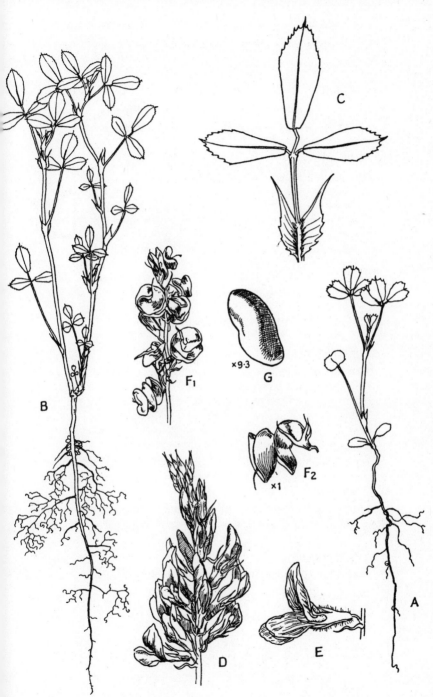

7

Ornithopus perpusillus (*Common Bird's-foot*)

A. *Floral organs.*

Time of flowering—June and July.

Inflorescence—2 to 4 flower heads at the end of long axillary branches.

Flowers—Almost sessile, subtended by a small leaf ; calyx 5, prominent teeth, hairy ; petals pinkish-white ; stamens 10, upper one free ; ovary slightly flattened, long, several ovules.

Fruit—Pods, slightly hairy, ending in a curved beak, separating when ripe into short, oval, one-seeded parts.

Seed—Yellow, oval with flattened ends.

B. *Vegetative organs.*

Seedling—Cotyledons above ground, long stalks ; first leaf compound, 4 to 5 pairs leaflets.

Habit of growth—Prostrate to sub-erect, annual.

Stems—6 to 12 inches long, round, slightly hairy.

Leaves—Compound ; leaflets 5 to 20 pairs, opposite, hairy ; lowest pair close to the stem ; stipules small.

Root system—Tap root, numerous fine, secondary branches.

C. *Distribution.*

Indigenous to Southern and Central Europe and Sweden. Most common in Britain in sandy and gravelly places.

D. *Economic value.*

Useful for green manuring on light, sandy soil.

Fig. 40.—A. Seedling. B. Complete plant. C. Leaf. D. Inflorescence. E. Floret. F_1. Collection of fruits. F_2. Portion of fruit. G. Seed.

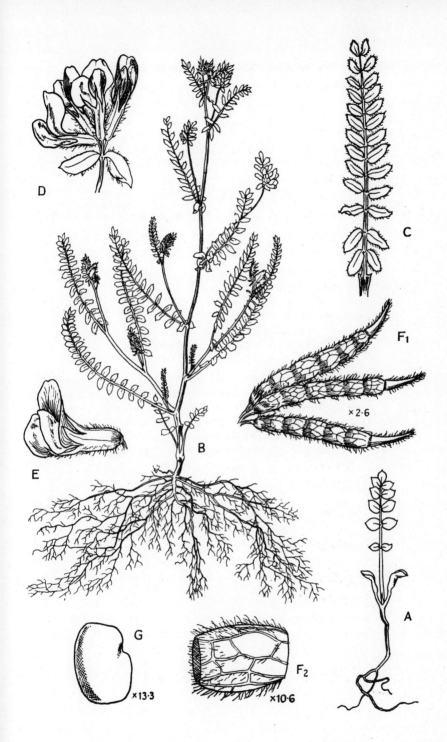

Onobrychis sativa (Sainfoin)

A. *Floral organs.*

Time of flowering—June and July.

Inflorescence—Compact raceme, borne on long axillary
branches ; later, flowers separate due to elongation of
stalk.

Florets—Pale pink with dark red veins about 1 inch long ;
calyx 5, long teeth ; petals 5—wing petals shorter than
keel and standard ; stamens 10, upper one free ; ovary
round, one ovule.
with veins ; lower edge bordered with short teeth ; one-
seeded.

Seed (milled)—Kidney shaped, prominent radicle, 4 to 5 mm.
long, greenish-brown, bright.

B. *Vegetative organs.*

Seedling—Cotyledons above ground, thick, fleshy, sessile ;
first leaf simple, oval, second leaf trifoliate, fourth leaf
pinnate.

Habit of growth—Erect perennial.

Stems—1 to 2 feet high, round, slightly hairy.

Leaves—Pinnate, 6 to 12 pairs leaflets, plus a terminal one,
slightly hairy below ; projecting mid-rib ; stipules thin,
finely-pointed, browning with age.

Root system—Tap root, long, thick and fleshy, numerous
nodules.

C. *Distribution.*

Indigenous to Southern Europe and temperate Asia. Most
common in Britain in south on calcareous soils.

D. *Economic value.*

Two varieties—(1) Common Sainfoin, (2) Giant Sainfoin.
Common Sainfoin persists for a number of years, cut for hay in
the first year, afterwards foraged or grazed. Giant Sainfoin
lasts for two years only, cut for hay, or foraged and grazed.
Both varieties are drilled with Barley on light calcareous soils
in the south. Rate of seeding 40 lb. milled and 100 lb. unmilled
per acre. Both varieties are deep rooted and drought resistant.

Fig. 41.—A. Seedling. B. Complete plant. C. Leaf. D. Inflorescence.
E. Floret. F_1. Collection of fruits. F_2. Single fruit (unmilled seed).
G. Seed.

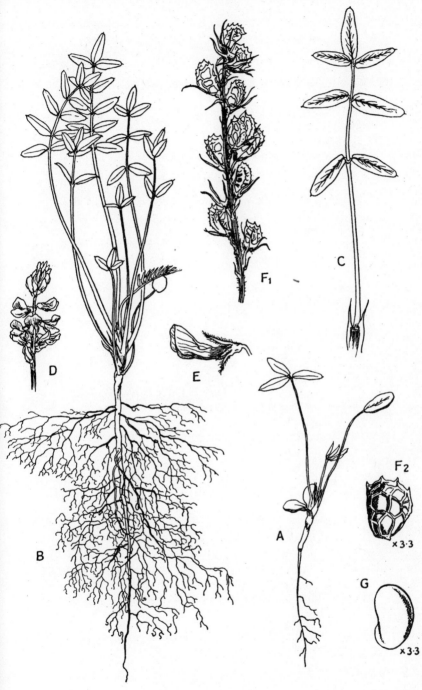

Poterium Sanguisorba (*Lesser Burnet*)

A. *Floral organs.*

Time of flowering—July.

Inflorescence—Flower heads arranged in dense ovate heads, at the end of long axillary stalks.

Flowers—Numerous, light green in colour, often with a reddish tinge ; lower flowers all males, upper ones female ; numerous hanging stamens ; long style, tufted stigma ; calyx 4 lobed ; petals absent ; ovary containing 1 or 2 ovules.

Fruit—Brown, quadrangular nut, irregularly pitted surfaces, usually one seed ; fruit often an impurity in unmilled Sainfoin seed.

Seed—Yellowish-brown, oval, pointed, flattened surface on one side, 2 mm. long.

B. *Vegetative organs.*

Seedling—Cotyledons above ground, long stalks, notched near petiole ; first leaf trifoliate, serrated edge.

Habit of growth—Erect perennial.

Stems—12 to 18 inches long, slightly hairy, angular.

Leaves—Compound, leaflets small, oval, serrated edges, slightly hairy.

Root system—Tap root, numerous stout branches.

C. *Distribution.*

In dry places and limestone clefts in Southern Europe, Asia and Sweden. Most common in Britain in limestone districts.

D. *Economic value.*

Nutritive value less than Sainfoin, which should replace it in seeds mixtures for light calcareous soils. Sainfoin and Burnet often grow together, and Burnet seed often occurs as an impurity in a Sainfoin sample. Burnet belongs to the Rosaceae family and does not possess nodules on its root system.

Fig. 42.—A. Seedling. B. Complete plant. C. Leaf. D. Inflorescence. F. Fruit. G. Seed.

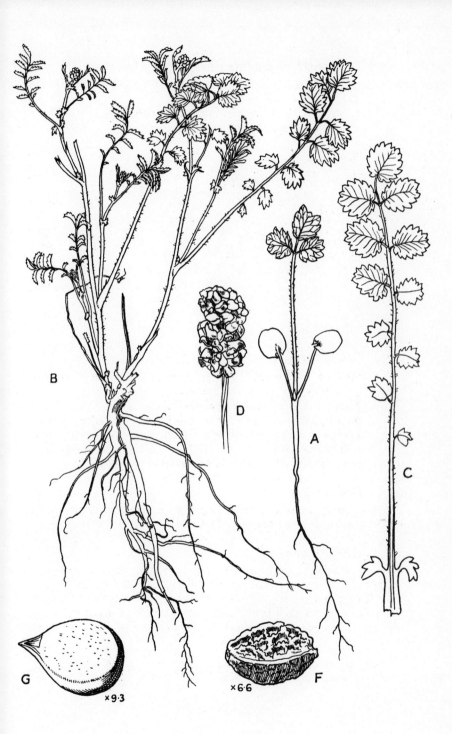

B

D

A

C

G

×9·3

×6·6

F

Trifolium dubium (*Yellow Suckling Clover*)

A. *Floral organs.*

Time of flowering—July.

Inflorescence—Small terminal raceme; round to oval in shape.

Florets—Yellow, numbering about 12 in each head; calyx 5, short teeth; petals 5, standard narrow; stamens 10; ovary one ovule; usually self-sterile.

Fruit—One-seeded pod.

Seed—Oval, radicle scarcely visible; about 1·5 mm. long; colour yellow to dark olive; shiny.

B. *Vegetative organs.*

Seedling—Cotyledons above ground, oval, distinctly stalked; first leaf glabrous, broader than long.

Habit of growth—Sub-erect to prostrate annual, sometimes persists two years.

Stems—Long, 18 to 24 inches, wiry, turning red.

Leaves—Trifoliate, short stalks; leaflets small, sometimes slightly hairy, the central leaflet with longer stalk than the other two; stipules broad at base, sharply pointed.

Root system—Short tap root, numerous nodules.

C. *Distribution.*

Indigenous to most of Europe. Most common in Britain in the south and east on poor soils.

D. *Economic value.*

On account of its low leaf production it is not recommended for sowing in seeds mixtures, except in small quantities, 2 to 4 lb. per acre, on light poor soils.

FIG. 43.—A. Seedling. B. Complete plant. C. Leaf. D. Inflorescence. E. Floret. F. Fruit. G. Seed.

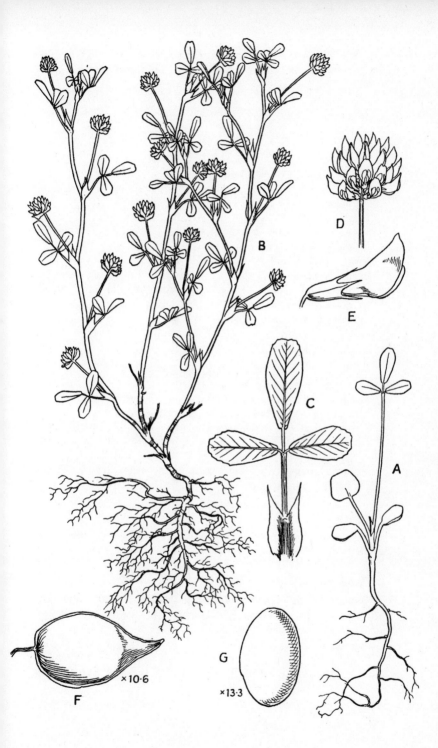

Trifolium hybridum (*Alsike Clover*)

A. *Floral organs.*

Time of flowering—June and July.

Inflorescence—Raceme globular, arising on long stalks spring-
ing from the axils of leaves on the main stem.

Florets—Pale pink or white ; calyx 5, equal length ; petals
5, free ; ovary containing 1 to 3 ovules ; self-sterile,
fertilised by bees.

Fruit—Pod, 1 to 3 seeds, indehiscent.

Seed—Heart-shaped, due to the radicle projecting to more
than half length of seed ; approximately 1 mm. long ;
greenish-brown in colour, becoming darker with age ;
bright, smooth.

B. *Vegetative organs.*

Seedling—Cotyledons above ground, oval ; first leaf simple,
almost oval, glabrous.

Habit of growth—Upright habit, persists 3 to 6 years.

Stems—Glabrous, branched, 2 to 3 feet high.

Leaves—Trifoliate ; leaflets obovate, glabrous ; lower edges
of leaflets slightly serrated ; stipules tapering to a point,
greenish veins.

Root system—Tap root, numerous secondary rootlets ;
nodules numerous.

C. *Distribution.*

Indigenous to Europe ; abundant in Sweden and Canada. Not
indigenous to Britain.

D. *Economic value.*

Sown in seeds mixtures in Britain on heavy damp soils, and
will usually thrive where Red Clover fails on account of soil
acidity and clover sickness.

FIG. 44.—A. Seedling. B. Complete plant. C. Leaf. D. Inflorescence.
E. Floret. F. Fruit. G. Seed.

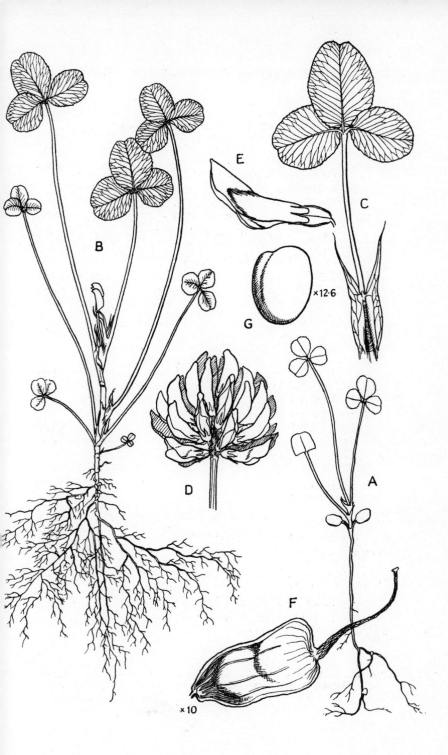

E

C

×12·6

B

G

D

A

F

×10

Trifolium incarnatum (*Crimson Clover, Trifolium*)

A. *Floral organs.*

Time of flowering—July.

Inflorescence—Terminal raceme, some distance above last leaf on stem, oblong to cylindrical, sometimes 2 inches long.

Florets—Rich crimson or white, calyx 5, long, hairy ; petals 5; stamens 10 ; ovary one ovule ; usually self-sterile, fertilised by bees.

Fruit—One-seeded pod.

Seed—Oval, radicle small and scarcely seen on outside ; 2·5 mm. long, shiny, yellowish-brown.

B. *Vegetative organs.*

Seedling—Cotyledons above ground ; first leaf large, broad, hairy, lobed at base.

Habit of growth—Erect annual.

Stems—1 to 2 feet high, extremely hairy, few side branches.

Leaves—Trifoliate, long stalks near base of stem ; leaflets obovate to obcordate, hairy ; stipules broad, blunt apex, the older stipules often possessing a purple margin.

Root system—Long, finely branched ; numerous nodules.

C. *Distribution.*

Indigenous in open places in Southern Europe. Not found wild in Britain, except for a wild white variety in Cornwall.

D. *Economic value.*

The Early Red and Late White varieties are used as catch crops or green manuring in the South of England. Sown after cereals in autumn, and fed off or cut for hay in June ; seed rate per acre about 20 lb. They are sometimes sown with Italian Rye-grass or Rye for silage.

FIG. 45.—A. Seedling. B. Complete plant. C. Leaf. D. Inflorescence. E. Floret. F. Fruit. G. Seed.

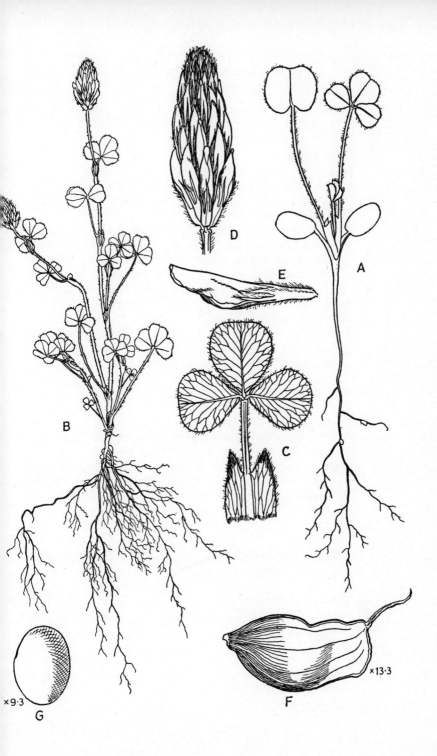

A

B

D

E

C

G
×9·3

F
×13·3

Trifolium pratense, spontaneum (Wild Red Clover)

A. *Floral organs.*

Time of flowering—April and May.

Inflorescence—Terminal raceme on main stem, oval to globular, 1 to 1½ inches long ; subtended by two almost sessile trifoliate leaves.

Florets—Approximately 30 in number, self-sterile, pollinated by bees, pink to various shades of red, calyx hairy, 5 teeth, inferior one longer than others ; petals 5, narrow, jointed at base, and attached to staminal tube of 9 stamens, the upper stamen free ; ovary small, 2 ovules.

Fruit—One-seeded pyxidium, splitting transversely in half to release seed.

Seed—Oval, 1·5 mm. to 2 mm. long ; shiny, upper half yellowish, lower half purple ; small projection near base covering radicle.

B. *Vegetative organs.*

Seedling—Cotyledons above ground, oval ; first leaf simple, round, hairy.

Habit of growth—Sub-erect to prostrate, straggly perennial.

Stems—Solid, wiry, may or may not possess hairs.

Leaves—Trifoliate ; leaflets ovate, dark green, sometimes hairy, with light markings on upper surface. Stipules membraneous, frequently with purple veins ; finely pointed.

Root system—Stout tap root ; numerous nodules.

C. *Distribution.*

Indigenous to Europe and Asia, and from Mediterranean to Arctic regions. Most common in Britain in fertile meadows.

D. *Economic value.*

On account of the low proportion of leaf to stem it is not recommended for seeds mixtures.

FIG. 46.—A. Seedling. B. Complete plant. C. Leaf. D. Inflorescence. E. Floret. F. Fruit. G. Seed.

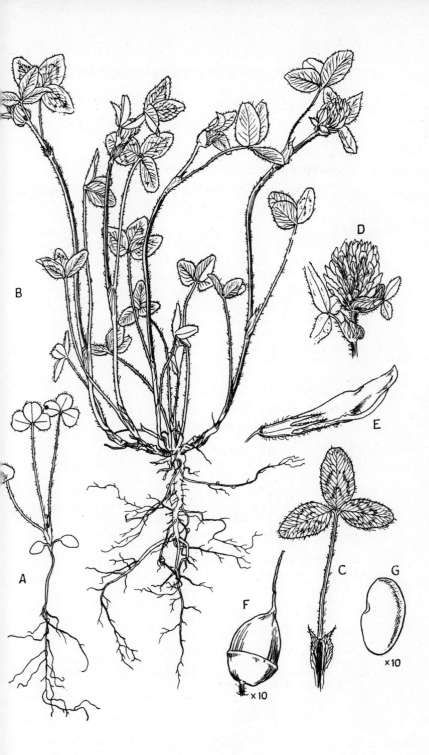

A

B

D

E

C

F ×10

G ×10

A. *Trifolium pratense, præcox* (*Broad Red Clover*)

Broad Red or Early-flowering Red Clover is a cultivated variety and differs from Wild Red in the following respects : (*a*) Time of flowering about 14 to 21 days later ; (*b*) leaves larger and distinctly broader ; (*c*) stems hollow, more erect, less numerous ; (*d*) persists for two years only ; (*e*) frequently sown in seeds mixtures on good soils for temporary leys of one or two years' duration ; (*f*) provides early spring growth and an excellent aftermath in the first year. When sown with Perennial Rye-grass it makes excellent silage.

During recent years numerous varieties have been compared at the Welsh Plant Breeding Station, Aberystwyth. Results have shown that the British varieties, viz. Dorset Marl, Vale of Clwyd, Vale of Glamorgan, Cotswold, Hampshire and S.151 are superior to imported varieties.

B. *Trifolium pratense, serotinum* (*Late-flowering Red Clover or Single-Cut Cow Grass*)

This variety is more persistent (4 to 5 years) and as a result is more widely cultivated than Broad Red. It often possesses more stems per plant and produces flowers about 14 days later. The first year's hay crop is usually heavy, but spring and aftermath growth is definitely below that of Broad Red. During the second and succeeding years it surpasses Broad Red in every respect. On account of its persistency and high productivity it is recommended for seeding permanent grass on good soils. Varieties are now arranged in three groups : (i) early-flowering or Single-cut Cow Grass, (ii) late-flowering reds, (iii) extra-late-flowering reds.

Fig. 47.—A. Seedling. B. Complete plant. C. Leaf. D. Inflorescence. E. Floret. F. Fruit. G. Seed.

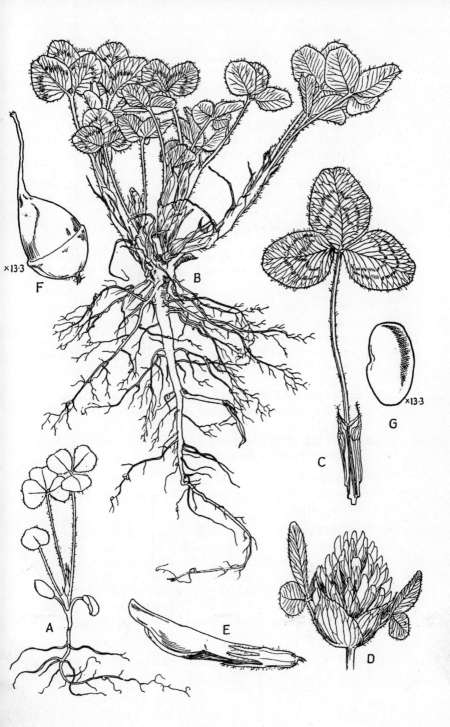

×13·3

F

B

C

×13·3

G

A

E

D

8

Trifolium repens (*White Clover*)

A. *Floral organs.*

Time of flowering—May to August.

Inflorescence—Almost spherical, produced at the end of long stalks, which spring from the axils of the leaves on the stolons.

Florets—White, sometimes tinged pink ; calyx 5, equal ; petals 5, joined to stamens at base, becoming brown and deflexed later ; ovary 4 to 6 ovules.

Fruit—Pod, 2 to 3 seeds, splitting along one side to release seeds.

Seed—Heart-shaped, radicle projecting to half the length of seed ; approximately 1 mm. long, bright yellow to yellowish-brown.

B. *Vegetative organs.*

Seedling—Cotyledons above ground, first leaf round, glabrous, slightly serrated edges.

Habit of growth—Prostrate creeping perennial, stoloniferous.

Stems—Solid, possessing adventitious roots at the nodes ; glabrous.

Leaves—Trifoliate, leaflets obovate, serrated edges, with or without markings on upper surface, glabrous ; stipules small, pointed.

Root system—Stout tap root on main plant, with adventitious roots on nodes of stems.

C. *Distribution.*

Indigenous to Europe and Asia. Common in Britain on all rich pastures.

D. *Economic value.*

Wild White Clover has small leaflets and is often sown in seeds mixtures for long leys. It has a high nutritive value and is very persistent. The large-leaved White Clover groups (S.100, Lodino, Kersey, Morso, and Dutch White) are more productive and less persistent, and are used in seeds mixtures for short leys for grazing and silage.

Fig. 48.—A. Seedling. B. Complete plant. C. Leaf. D. Inflorescence. E. Floret. F. Fruit. G. Seed.

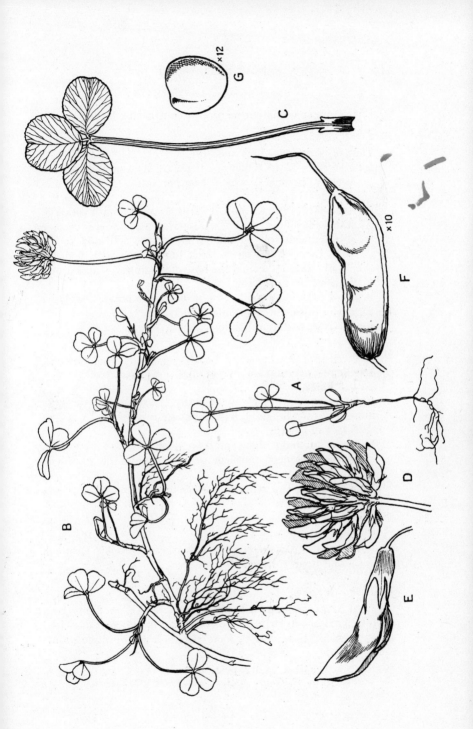

Trifolium subterraneum (*Subterranean Clover*)

A. *Floral organs.*

Time of flowering—June and July.

Inflorescence—2 to 5 flowers together, at the end of long axillary branches, which lengthen after flowering and turn downwards.

Florets—White or pale pink ; calyx 5, teeth long ; petals 5, standard long ; after fertilisation the flowers become reversed and rest on the surface of the soil, and at the same time several short thick fibres, each with 5 teeth, rapidly develop around the base of the flower, which firmly fix the fruit in the soil.

Fruit—Pod, one-seeded, 2 to 3 pods may be present, enclosed in the thick fibres forming a burr.

Seed—Oval, dark purplish in colour.

B. *Vegetative organs.*

Seedling—Cotyledons above ground, long erect stalks ; first leaf hairy.

Habit of growth—Prostrate annual.

Stems—Prostrate, stout, hairy, sometimes reaching from 4 to 6 feet in length.

Leaves—Trifoliate, long stalks ; leaflets hairy, obovate, often prominent purplish veins ; stipules broad, finely pointed.

Root system—Tap root, numerous nodules, no adventitious roots at nodes.

C. *Distribution.*

Indigenous to dry sandy soils in Southern Europe. Common in South and Central England.

D. *Economic value.*

Used in Australia as a fodder plant. Would probably be a useful ingredient in British seeds mixtures if sufficient care were taken to permit re-seeding by removing stock at time of flowering.

Fig. 49.—A. Seedling. B. Complete plant. C. Leaf. D. Changes in position of floral organs. E. Burr. F. Fruit. G. Seed.

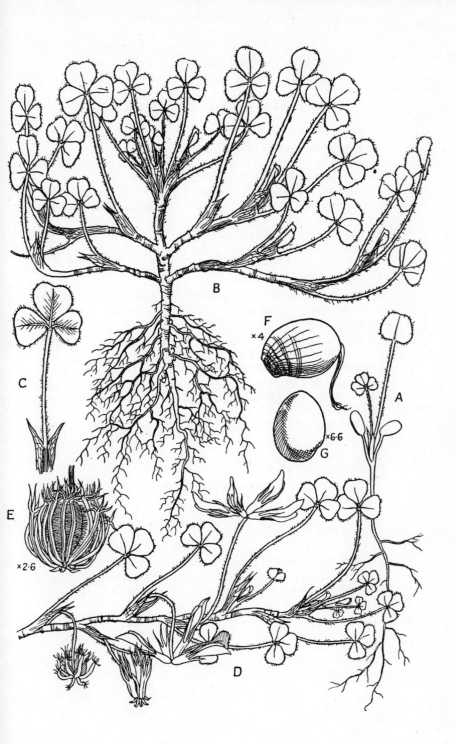

B

F
×4

C

A

E
×2·6

G
×6·6

D

Vicia sativa (Common Vetch)

A. *Floral organs.*

Time of flowering—Spring and early summer.

Inflorescence—Flowers borne singly, or in pairs on short stalks in the axil of leaves on the main stem.

Flowers—Large, calyx 5 teeth, hairy; petals 5, reddish-purple; stamens 10, upper one free; ovary sometimes hairy, 4 to 10 ovules.

Fruit—Pod, 1 to 2 inches long, 4 to 10 seeds.

Seed—Dark brown, 5 mm. long, round.

B. *Vegetative organs.*

Seedling—Cotyledons remain below ground; first leaf with one pair leaflets, no tendrils.

Habit of growth—Trailing annual.

Stems—Numerous, long, nearly erect, almost climbing, weak, square, and slightly hairy.

Leaves—Pinnate, alternate on stems; 6 to 7 pairs opposite leaflets, mucronate tip, tendrils branched; stipules toothed, pointed, with sometimes a dark purple blotch in centre.

Root system—Tap root, slender, branching freely; nodules large.

C. *Distribution.*

Indigenous to Europe and certain parts of Asia. Most common in Britain on dry soils.

D. *Economic value.*

Two cultivated varieties: winter- and spring-sown. Both varieties are used for green fodder, either sown alone or with Oats, Barley, Rye or Beans (2 bushels of Oats to 1½ bushels of Vetches). Vetches make a very useful green feed for sheep and other live stock.

Fig. 50.   A. Seedling.   B. Complete plant.   C. Leaf.   E. Flower.   F. Fruit. G. Seed.

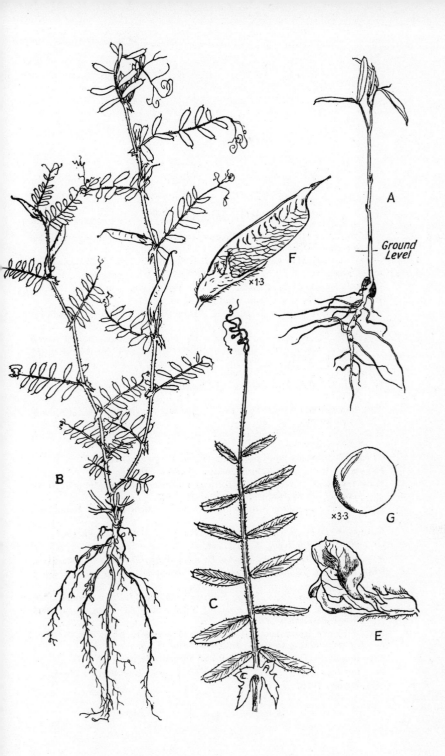

A

Ground
Level

F
×1·3

B

C

G
×3·3

E

BIBLIOGRAPHY

AGRICULTURE, MINISTRY OF. *Weeds of Grassland* by H. C. Long. Bulletin No. 41. H.M.S.O.

— *Grassland Management.* 2nd ed. Bulletin No. 154. H.M.S.O.

ARMSTRONG, S. F. *British Grasses.* Cambridge University Press, 1937.

Collins-Longmans' Study Atlas. 14th ed. Collins and Longmans, 1962.

DAVIES, W. *The Grass Crop.* 2nd ed. Spon, 1960.

Dunns Guide to Farm Grasses. 1962. (Dunns Farm Seeds Ltd., Salisbury, Wilts.)

FAGAN, T. W. and MILTON, W. E. J. 'The chemical composition of eleven species and strains of grasses at different stages of maturity'. *Welsh J. Agric.*, 1931.

HUBBARD, C. E. *Grasses.* Penguin, 1954.

IVINS, J. D. *The Measurement of Grassland Productivity.* Butterworth, 1959.

THE LAND UTILISATION SURVEY. *The Land of Britain.* Geographical Publications.

MERCER, S. P. 'The rye grass seed industry of Northern Ireland'. *Agricultural Progress,* 1949.

'Methods of pasture analysis'. *Agricultural Progress,* 1933.

PERCIVAL, JOHN. *Agricultural Botany.* Duckworth, 1936.

ROBERTS, R. A. 'Studies in the formation of permanent pastures in North Wales.' *Welsh Journal of Agriculture,* 1926.

PEEL, W. R. *Grassland Management for the Practical Farmer.* Macmillan, 1938.

ROBINSON, D. H. *Leguminous Forage Plants.* 2nd ed. Arnold, 1947.

— *The New Farming.* Faber, 1951.

STAPLEDON, R. G. *The Plough-up Policy and Ley-Farming.* Faber, 1959.

STAPLEDON, R. G. and HANLEY, J. A. *Grassland.* Oxford University Press, 1927.

THOMAS, J. O. *Grassland. Young Farmers' Club* Booklet No. 6. Evans, 1959.

WATSON, J. A. SCOTT. *The Farming Year.* New ed. Longmans, 1963 (Rural Education Series).

WELSH PLANT BREEDING STATION, Plas Gogerddan, Aberystwyth. *The Hybridisation of Grasses.* Bulletin Series H., No. 2.

— *Red Clover Investigations* 1919-26. Bulletin Series H., No. 7.

— *Varieties and Strains of Red and White Clover.* Bull. Ser. H., No. 16.

— *Report,* 1962.

GLOSSARY

Aggressive species.—One that grows rapidly and tends to smother out other species in the sward, e.g. Italian Rye-grass.

Asperites.—Little projections on the leaves, making them harsh and unpalatable.

Awn.—An extension of the pale into a bristle-like appendage.

Bacteria.—Unicellular, non-green organism, usually classified in the Plant Kingdom.

Bifoliate.—A leaf possessing two leaflets.

Bract.—A modified leaf.

Carpel.—A one-celled seed vessel, or one of the component members of a compound pistil or seed vessel.

Caryopsis.—A fruit in which the seed-coat is fused to the ovary wall.

Chromosomes.—The rod-shaped bodies into which a cell nucleus separates when the cell itself is about to divide. The chromosomes carry the genes.

Cleistogamous.—Flowers which never expand and are systematically self-fertilised.

Coleoptile.—The first leaf to appear when grasses germinate.

Coleorhiza.—The sheath which encloses the young rootlets of grasses when they germinate.

Commercial seed.—The seeds of grasses are usually sold in the form of fruits. (See Caryopsis.)

Cotyledons.—A seed leaf or first leaf of the embryo. According to the number of cotyledons, plants may be monocotyledonous or dicotyledonous.

Cross fertilise.—The male gametes of one plant fertilising the female gamete of another plant.

Downy.—Covered with short soft hairs.

Embryo.—The rudimentary form of any living thing in its first stage of development.

Endosperm.—Food reserve material in seeds.

Enzyme.—A chemical compound of vegetable or animal origin, which is capable of creating a chemical change, yet in itself remaining unchanged in the process.

Epicotyl.—The portion of a young stem of an embryo above the cotyledons.

Filament.—Stalk.

Gamete.—Sex cell: male or female.

Genes.—Those parts of a chromosome's substance that control the characters of an organism.

Germination.—The first act of growth in a seed.

Glabrous.—Without hairs.

Glaucous.—With a bluish-green colour and a shiny bloom.

Glume.—A chaff-like scale or bract enclosing the flowers of grasses.

Gramineae.—The botanical family of grasses.

Hirsute.—When hairs are dense and not stiff.

Hypocotyl.—The part of the stem of a young plant below the cotyledons.

Hypogynous.—When the stalks of the stamens arise below the ovary on the axis of a flower.

Indigenous.—Plants which are native to, and grow wild in a country.

Inflorescence.—Flowers borne collectively on an axis.

Internode.—The part between two nodes or joints of a stem.

Leguminosae.—The botanical family to which clovers, medicks, vetches, etc., belong.

Lemma.—The bract that is called, in this book, the outer pale.

Ley.—Sown down to grass in a rotation of crops.

Lodicule.—A delicate scale found between the stamens and pales in grasses.

Membraneous.—A thin sheet-like structure, usually translucent.

Morphology.—A study of the form and structure of plants and animals.

Motor cells.—Thin walled cells near the mid-rib of grasses, semi-transparent and capable of losing and gaining water, which control the expansion of the leaves, and loss of moisture from the plant.

Mucronate.—Ending abruptly in a short, sharp point.

Nitrogen.—A tasteless, odourless, colourless, inactive gas; but in a solid and combined form can be a plant food.

Node.—Joint of a stem.

Obcordate.—Heart-shaped leaf, with the notch opposite the stem.

Obovate.—Inversely ovate, leaf with point of attachment at the narrow end.

Ovary.—The female organ of plants and animals in which are produced the unfertilised seed or eggs.

Pales.—The bracts of a grass flower.

Palea.—The bract that is called, in this book, the inner pale.

Plumule.—The first bud of an embryo, or the first bud above the cotyledons.

Pollen.—Dust-like grains formed within the anthers of flowers; the male element of flowering plants.

Pubescent.—See " Downy."

Radicle.—Root-like part of an embyro.

Rhizome.—A creeping subterranean stem, usually producing roots and leaves at its nodes.

"S" Varieties.—Varieties bred from wild or indigenous species.

Scutellum.—The supposed cotyledon of grass seeds, lying between the embryo and endosperm.

Self-fertile.—A flower which fertilises itself.

Self-sterile.—A flower which is incapable of fertilising itself.

Stamen.—The pollen-bearing organ of a flower.

Stigma.—The part of a pistil which receives the pollen.

Stipule.—One of the pair of appendages found at the base of a petiole of certain leaves, e.g. *Leguminosae* family.

Stolon.—A creeping stem above ground, which usually roots at the nodes.

Sward.—A turf, or the surface of soil thickly covered with grass and clover.

Tendril.—A slender leafless organ produced by the modification of a stem or leaf, and which enables the plant to climb and coil itself round a support.

Tetraploid.—A plant with four sets of chromosomes instead of the more usual two.

Tiller.—A shoot from the base of a stem.

TABLE OF SOME "S" VARIETIES. See pages 10-11

S.22.	Italian Rye-grass	S.101.	Perennial Rye-grass
S.23.	Perennial Rye-grass	S.123.	Red Clover
S.24.	Perennial Rye-grass	S.143.	Cocksfoot
S.26.	Cocksfoot	S.151.	Red Clover
S.37.	Cocksfoot	S.170.	Tall Fescue
S.48.	Timothy	S.184.	White Clover
S.50.	Timothy	S.215.	Meadow Fescue
S.51.	Timothy	S.321.	Perennial Rye-grass
S.53.	Meadow Fescue	S.345.	Cocksfoot
S.59.	Red Fescue	S.352.	Timothy
S.100.	White Clover		

This list is certain to be extended as time passes.

INDEX TO PLANT NAMES